Perfecting the Point

Place value, Decimals, & Percentages

by
Letz Farmer

Mastery Publications
90 Hillside Lane
Arden, NC 28704-9709
(828) 684-0429

ISBN 0-929223-06-3

DEDICATION

The MASTERING MATHEMATICS series is dedicated to:

my parents, who encouraged me,

my husband and daughter, who supported me, and

my heavenly Father Who gave me the skills to create.

ABOUT THE AUTHOR

Mrs. Letz Farmer is a Christian wife and home schooling mother, former resource teacher/ curriculum developer, and writer. She holds a bachelor's degree in mental retardation, and additional graduate work and experience in learning disabilities, emotional disturbance, deafness, and gifted and talented.

The **MASTERING MATHEMATICS** series grew out of the void she noted in individualized math programs for Christian home schoolers. Children with special needs were suffering the same failure and/or boredom using standardized home schooling curricula that they experienced in their previous school situations. This individualized basic math curriculum was developed in the hopes of remediating problems and preventing others.

PLACE VALUE

☞ USE THE NUMBER **84739.26501** TO ANSWER THESE QUESTIONS.

What digit is in the:

(A) tens place = _____

(B) hundredths place =_____

(C) ten thousands place =_____

(D) ones (units) place =_____

(E) thousandths place =_____

(F) tenths place =_____

Round the number to the nearest:

(G) thousandth =_____

(H) tenth =_____

(I) hundredth =_____

Put these numbers in order from smallest to largest:

(J) .424   .4   .4142 =_____

(K) 54.3713   54.376   54.3 =_____

Write this amount as a number:

(L) 4.28 million =_____

ADDITION

(M) 24.63
  + 18.76

(N) 14.6 +8.593 =

(O) 76.2 + 9 +.286=

(P) Jill's team swam the butterfly in 33.7, 33.593, 34.4 and 33.98 seconds. What was their total time (in seconds)?_____ Which was the slowest time?_____ The fastest time?_____

SUBTRACTION

(Q) Using Jill's team (question P), what was the time difference between the fastest and slowest swimmer?_____

(R) 23.493
  - 6.532

(S) 78.3 - .97 =

(T) 5801 - 4.362 =

MULTIPLICATION
☞   ROUND ALL MULTIPLICATION ANSWERS TO THE NEAREST HUNDREDTH.

(U) 41.23
x   6

(V) 26.9
x   4.3

(W) .389
x   .12

DIVISION

(X) 3)‾6.819‾

(Y) .5)‾4.795‾

(Z) .9)‾747‾

(AA) .2)‾6.91‾

(BB) 2.4)‾50‾

PERCENTAGES
(CC) Change 53% to a decimal number =_____
(DD) Write 8.7 as a percentage =_____
(EE) Write 6.9% as a decimal number =_____
(FF) Find 45% of $250.00 = _____
(GG) If you tithed 10% of $65, how much would you give?_____
                          How much would you have left?_____
(HH) Mark wants a $23.95 sleeping bag. Sales tax is 5.5%.   Rounded to the nearest cent, how much will his total cost be?_____
(II) 18 is what % of 24?_____
(JJ) Sam **won** 15 of his 24 races. What percentage did he **lose**?_____
(KK) 30 is 75% of what number?_____

SUGGESTED ENTRY LEVELS

The PRETEST has been broken down into sections that correspond with the major sections of the workbook. The problem where your child's first error occurs indicates where his/her strengths becomes weaknesses.

Beside each problem is a corresponding letter or letters. Circle the letter(s) your child missed. Note the **first error** your child made in each section.   That **EARLIEST** page number is the student's **suggested entry level** for that section.

PLACE VALUE

(A) PAGE 3   (G) PAGE 62
(B) PAGE 19   (H) PAGE 62
(C) PAGE 13   (I) PAGE 62
(D) PAGE 1   (J) PAGE 24
(E) PAGE 2   (K) PAGE 25
(F) PAGE 16   (L) PAGE 29

SUGGESTED ENTRY PAGE _____

ADDITION

(M) PAGE 31   (N) PAGE 37   (O) PAGE 40   (P) PAGE 39

SUGGESTED ENTRY PAGE _____

SUBTRACTION

(Q) PAGE 47   (R) PAGE 42   (S) PAGE 45   (T) PAGE 46

SUGGESTED ENTRY PAGE _____

MULTIPLICATION

(U) PAGE 56   (V) PAGE 57   (W) PAGE 58

CORRECT ANSWER BUT ROUNDING ERRORS - PAGE 62

SUGGESTED ENTRY PAGE _____

DIVISION

(X) PAGE 80   (Y) PAGE 82   (Z) PAGE 84
(AA) PAGE 89   (BB) PAGE 91

SUGGESTED ENTRY PAGE _____

PERCENTAGES

(CC) PAGE 68   (DD) PAGE 96   (EE) PAGE 69   (FF) PAGE 71
(GG) PAGE 73   (HH) PAGE 74   (II) PAGE 101   (JJ) PAGE 75
(KK) PAGE 109

SUGGESTED ENTRY PAGE _____

When God created people, He gave them a wonderful body. This body came equipped with something special for counting - fingers. Fingers were easy to see and count, by pointing up or curling them out of sight. Today, many people still use them occasionally.

People all over the world have different ways to count. Some primitive civilizations don't need many number concepts. They don't use man-made money. They use a barter economy, trading hides, food, or their work for something they want. These people only use the simple number concepts of "one", "two", and "more".   They have a hard life, but an easy number system.

Our number system is much more complex and is based on the ten fingers God gave us. Your fingers are called _digits_. Each written number in our number system is also called a _digit_. Our digits include **0, 1, 2, 3, 4, 5, 6, 7, 8,** and **9**. The smallest digit is 0 (or nothing) and the largest digit is 9.

Does that mean we can't count any higher than 9? Absolutely not! We have learned to combine these digits into a number system which is infinite (never ending). Why, there are so many numbers (or **numerals)** that any number you can think of, someone else can think of a higher one. We never run out of numbers.

So how did we take ten little digits and make all of those numbers? Let's find out.

When writing numbers, you have been taught to write neatly. You can't write numbers on top of each other and still read them. You learned to write one digit in one space. This space is called a **place**. Single numbers, like 5, need a single place. Longer numbers, like 426, require 3 places - one place for each digit in the numeral.

Here are two digits - 0 and 1. Let's make some numbers out of them:

        01   10   100   1,000   10,000

What happened to the digit **1**? It moved to new **places**. It started in the last place on the right and ended up several places over on the left. As it moved, its **value** changed. It started out worth one, and then increased to ten, one hundred, one thousand, and ten thousand. In our number system, the **place** that a digit occupies gives you its **value**. This is called **place value**.

Here is a list of the **whole number** place values you will learn. You will begin with the smallest place (ONES) and work up to the TEN THOUSANDS place.

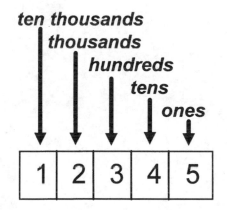

☞   Look at the number in the boxes above. What digit is in the:

(1) ones place = _____

(2) hundreds place = _____

(3) ten thousands place = _____

(4) tens place = _____

(5) thousands place = _____

Write the ten digits in our number system._____

You are now ready to begin learning **place value**. A digit gets its value from the place it is in. Each place has a name to help you remember how much value (or worth) to give to the digit.

ONES
0
1
2
3
4
5
6
7
8
9

The first places we will study are called the **UNITS**. The UNITS contain **three places**. What should we name the first place in the UNITS? Well, digits begin with the number 0, which is worth nothing. A place value worth nothing wouldn't be worth much, would it? We must look a little farther for a number that we can name our place after.

The smallest number that has worth is **1**. Therefore, your first place value is called **_ONES_**. The column of numbers in the box contains all the possible digits in the **ONES** place. The smallest number is _____. The largest number is _____. The **ONES** place, like all places, is **one digit wide** and <u>cannot</u> hold two digits.

Here are some sample numbers. The **_ONES_** place digit has been **darkened**.

<u>**5**</u>

6**4**

$853.1**3**6

Notice that the **ONES** place is **always** the **last digit** in a whole number. If the number has a decimal point, the **ONES** place is to the **left** of the **decimal**. It remains the **last digit** on the whole number side of the decimal point.

Now you will see how **the place a digit fills gives the digit its value**.

All of the digits 0-9 can be found in the **ONES** place. Let's use the digit 5 as an example. We will use words, numbers, and pictures.

5 = 5 ones = 1+1+1+1+1 = 5   □ □ □ □ □

☞ Look at the example. Write each word or number. Then draw the blocks at the end.

(1) 2 = *2 ones = 1+1 = 2*   □ □

(2) 7 =

(3) 0 =

(4) 4 =

(5) 9 =

(6) 3 =

(7) 8 =

(8) 6 =

(9) 1 =

Numbers 0 through 9 only require one place. They can fit into the ONES PLACE. The next number, "10", however, has **two digits** and takes up **two places**. The number "10" cannot be crammed into a single space. So, beginning with 10, you will need **two** places to write a number. You'll still keep the ONES PLACE, but will add another place **in front** of it. Since 10 is the first number to need two places, we will name the second place value of the UNITS *TENS*.

TENS	
↓ ones	
0	0
1	1
2	2
3	3
4	4
5	5
6	6
7	7
8	8
9	9

Your two place values in the UNITS now look like the example in the box. The **ONES** place is still on the end. The **TENS** place is now in front of it. You <u>cannot</u> fill the TENS place without putting something in the ONES place.

To show you how the **TENS place** works, let's use the number 24 as an example. Look at the two columns in the box. Each column has a place value name. The digit 2 is in the _____ place and the digit 4 is in the _____ place.

$$2 \text{ tens} = 10+10 = \_\_\_\_ \longrightarrow 20$$
$$4 \text{ ones} = 1+1+1+1 = \_\_\_\_ \longrightarrow \underline{+\ 4}$$

When you add the TENS place answer (____) to the ONES place answer (____), you should get the number you started with, _____.

The largest number you can write using both the TENS place and the ONES place is _____.

Let's use place value to show that each of these numbers equals itself. Here are some examples:

        TENS   ONES
14 =   1   4   =   1 ten = 10   10
                           4 ones=1+1+1+1=4   <u>+ 4</u>
                                                      14

6 =   0   6   =   no tens = 0   0
                           6 ones =1+1+1+1+1+1= <u>+ 6</u>

30 =   3   0   =   3 tens = 10+10+10 =   30
                           0 ones = 0   <u>+ 0</u>

Now turn to pages 4 and 5. Work the problems.

PERFECTING THE POINT   PLACE VALUE   NAME_____
                                            DATE_____

☞   Write the numbers these pictures represent.

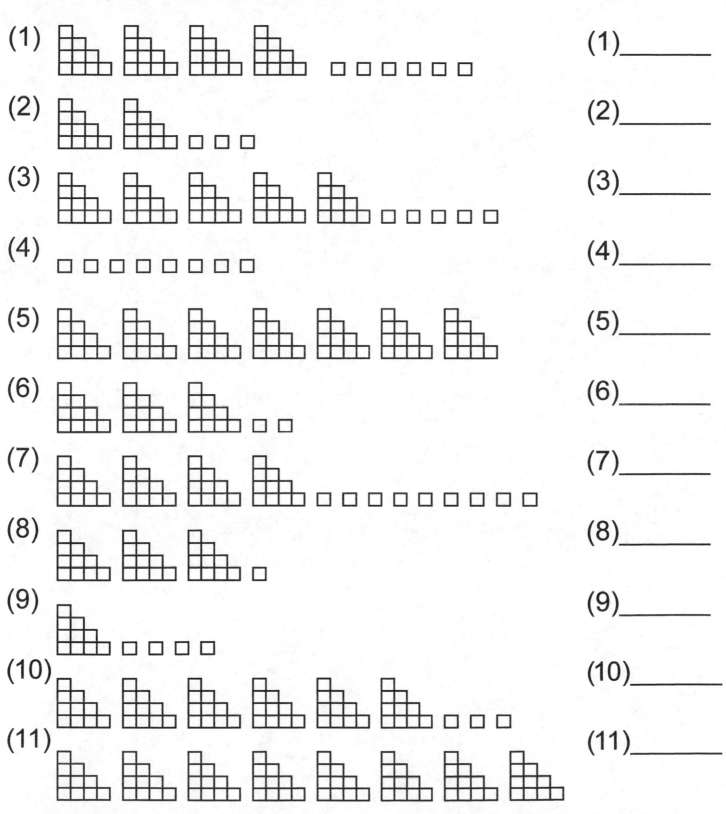

(1)_____
(2)_____
(3)_____
(4)_____
(5)_____
(6)_____
(7)_____
(8)_____
(9)_____
(10)_____
(11)_____

Number sentences have numbers instead of words. Here are two picture examples. Below the examples are the numbers sentences which explain what is happening.

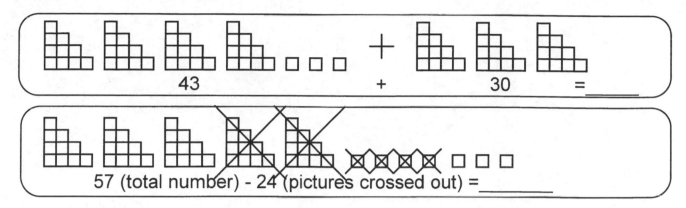

43   +   30   =_____

57 (total number) - 24 (pictures crossed out) =_____

☞ Now it's your turn. Write the number sentences for these pictures.

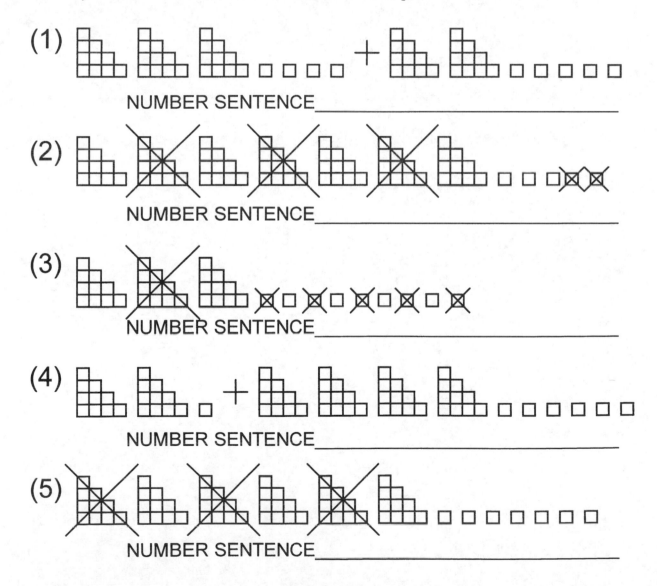

(1)   NUMBER SENTENCE_____

(2)   NUMBER SENTENCE_____

(3)   NUMBER SENTENCE_____

(4)   NUMBER SENTENCE_____

(5)   NUMBER SENTENCE_____

Sometimes, computers require you to make a one place number into a two place number.

For example, computers like dates written in a MM/DD/YY format. This means a two place number for the month (MM), a two place number for the day (DD), and a two place number for the year (YY). The problem is: sometimes the month or day is only a one place number. How do you change a one place number into two places? With **zero place holders**!

Let's pretend today's date is **Sept. 14, 1993**. First, we find the month (Sept.) and decide what number it is. Jan. is 1. What number month is Sept.?_____

Now we must change Sept. to a two place number. We can add a zero (which is worth nothing) to the number, but we must put it in the right place. Do we put the zero place holder before (09) or after the 9 (90)?_____

Well, which one says 9 - 09 or 90?_____ So, MM=_____ (no tens + 9 ones). Write the correct number in the correct box. Then darken the correct circle underneath.

Our day (DD) is 14, a two place number. That's easy. Put the digit 1 in the _____ column and the digit 4 in the _____ column. So DD=_____ (1 ten + 4 ones). Fill in the boxes and darken the correct circles.

Our year is 1993, a four place number. The 19-- is the name of the century, so do worry about that. The last two digits (the TENS place and the ONES place) are the important numbers. Put the digit 9 in the _____ place and the digit 3 in the _____ place. So, YY=_____ (9 tens + 3 ones). Now finish the sample date.

This sample date computer grid is a bit different than most. The numbers have been limited to the possibilities. Months run from 01 to 12. Days run from 01 to 31. Years can be any number from 00 (meaning 1900) to 99 (meaning 1999).

SAMPLE DATE

MONTH	DAY	YEAR
0 0	0 0	0 0
1 1	1 1	1 1
2 2	2 2	2 2
3 3	3 3	3 3
4	4	4 4
5	5	5 5
6	6	6 6
7	7	7 7
8	8	8 8
9	9	9 9

☞ Write the following dates in MM/DD/YY format.

(1) Oct. 5, 1949   (1) *10/05/49*

(2) Jan. 6, 1984   (2)_____

(3) May 16, 1901   (3)_____

(4) Your birthdate   (4)_____

(5) Your Mom's birthdate (5)_____

(6) Your Dad's birthdate (6)_____

(7) Another relative's birthdate (7)_____

(8) A friend's birthdate (8)_____

(9) A special date (what_____)(9)_____

(10) Today's date   (10)_____

Computers need time written in a special format - HH/MM. The hours (HH) and the minutes (MM) must be written as two place numbers. If only a single number is there, put a **zero in front** of it to make it a two place number.

Time, however, has its own special problem. The same times happen twice a day. There is an 8:30 a.m. (in the morning) and an 8:30 p.m. (at night). We can remember times easily by thinking A.M. means **at** **m**orning and P.M. means **p**ast **m**orning. But how can you let the computer know which 8:30 you mean when it only recognizes numbers?

The military solved this problem long before personal computers were invented. All A.M. (at morning) times were written in the regular way, but without a colon. Here are some examples of military time and how to say it:

9:00am = 0900 ("Oh nine hundred hours")

11:30am = 1130 ("eleven thirty hours")

P.M. (past morning) times begin at 12 o'clock noon (12:00pm). Noon (12:00) means that twelve hours and no minutes of the day are finished. This equals 1200 (**12** hours/**00** minutes) written in HH/MM format.

Through 12:59pm (59 minutes after noon), you don't need to do anything different (because the 1200 has already been added to the 59 minutes = 1259). Beginning at 1:00pm, however, your times begin to repeat. So you just add 1200 (12 hours and no minutes) to the p.m. time you to get military time. Here is how you do it:

1:00 pm =   1:00   10:35pm =   10:35

+ 12 00   + 12 00

13 00   22 35

So 1:00pm = 1300   So 10:35pm = 2235

("thirteen hundred hours")   ("twenty-two thirty-five hours")

☞   Write these times in HH/MM format. Be sure to pay attention to your a.m. and p.m. helpers.

(1) 7:03 a.m.   (1)_____

(2) 6:45 p.m.   (2)_____

(3) 12:38 a.m.   (3)_____

(4) 9:25 p.m.   (4)_____

(5) 11:09 p.m.   (5)_____

(6) 8:58 p.m.   (6)_____

(7) 2:01 p.m.   (7)_____

(8) 2:00 a.m.   (8)_____

(9) your bedtime   (9)_____

(10) time you got up today(10)_____

The numbers 10 through 99 all require two places. They fit in the TENS place and the ONES place with no digits left over. If you want to write numeral larger than 99, you must know the name of the UNITS' **largest** and **last place value**.

The first number to require **three** places is 100, another multiple of 10 (10 groups of 10 equal 100). Each new place is named after the first number which needs it. Guess what your new place value's name is?_____

Your place values now look like this: HUNDREDS tens ones

Here are some examples:

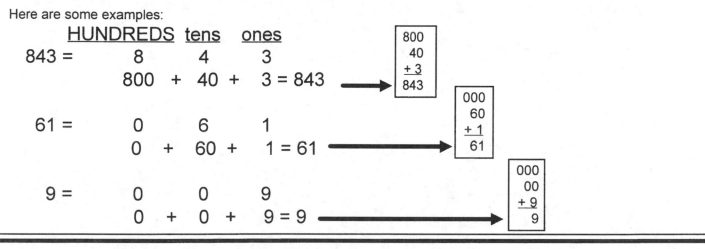

☞ Here are some numbers. Write the digits under each correct place value column. If there is no digit for that place or the digit is zero, write a zero in that column.

(1) 463
(2) 35
(3) 9
(4) 208
(5) 17
(6) 831
(7) 4
(8) 62
(9) 0
(10) 769

	hundreds	tens	ones
(1)			
(2)			
(3)			
(4)			
(5)			
(6)			
(7)			
(8)			
(9)			
(10)			

It is time to practice place value. Here is your first example:

462=___?___ hundreds =100+100+100+100 =   400

___?___ tens =10+10+10+10+10+10 =   60

___?___ ones = 1+1 =   +   2

☞   Work these problems just like the example above.

(1) 358 = _____ hundreds =

_____ tens =

_____ ones =

(2) 60 = _____ hundreds =

_____ tens =

_____ ones =

(3) 974 = _____ hundreds =

_____ tens =

_____ ones =

(4) 401 = _____ hundreds =

_____ tens =

_____ ones =

(5) 7 = _____ hundreds =

_____ tens =

_____ ones =

☞   Look at the numbers in the answer box.   Choose the correct number that has the digit:

6 in the tens place   (1)___*360*___

3 in the hundreds place   (2)_____

5 in the tens place   (3)_____

0 in the ones place   (4)_____

4 in the hundreds place   (5)_____

3 in the tens place   (6)_____

2 in the ones place   (7)_____

1 in the hundreds place   (8)_____

9 in the ones place   (9)_____

5 in the hundreds place   (10)_____

ANSWER BOX

526

360

19

934

402

153

☞   Read the following sentences.   Do what is asked.   Write your new number in the answer space.
example: Your number is 506.   Add 1 to the digit in the <u>ones</u> place.   What is your new number?_____
think: What digit is in the ones place? *(6)* By adding 1 to the 6, the ones place becomes 7.   I do nothing to the other places, so my new number is **507**.   (Hint: increase also means to make bigger, and is another word for add.)

(11) Your number is 254. Add 1 to the digit in the <u>hundreds</u> place. What is your new number?_____

(12) Your number is 620. Increase the <u>ones</u> place by 1. What is your new number?_____

(13) Your number is 387. Add 1 to the digit in the <u>tens</u> place. What is your new number?_____

(14) Your number is 109. Increase the <u>hundreds</u> place by 1. What is your new number?_____

(15) Your number is 925. Add 1 to the digit in the <u>tens</u> place. What is your new number?_____

The HUNDREDS, TENS, and ONES places are very important places to remember. The **order** of these three place names are repeated in every place value grouping from here on. Here is the pattern:

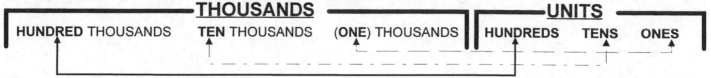

Now you are ready to learn about the next group of three places. The numbers 0 through 999 all fit into the first three places. The first number that requires **four** places is 1,000. The THOUSANDS place column goes **in front** of the HUNDREDS, and is usually separated by a comma.

When you are talking about the THOUSANDS place, you mean **ONE THOUSAND** or the **first** THOUSAND. The *one* in the THOUSANDS place is understood. This means that you know the one is there without ever saying the word "one". This concept makes sense when you say a number. Here are some THOUSANDS examples and the way we say them:

6,000 = "six thousand", not "six *one* thousand"

3,100 = "three thousand one hundred", not "three *one* thousand one hundred"

Here are some examples using the THOUSANDS place:

	THOUSANDS	hundreds	tens	ones
5,289=	5	2	8	9
641=	0	6	4	1
8003=	8	0	0	3

☞   Look at the numbers in the answer box. Choose the correct numeral that has the digit:

0 in the tens place   (1)_____

9 in the hundreds place   (2)_____

6 in the ones place   (3)_____

5 in the hundreds place   (4)_____

3 in the thousands place   (5)_____

7 in the tens place   (6)_____

4 in the ones place   (7)_____

1 in the hundreds place   (8)_____

9 in the thousands place   (9)_____

3 in the tens place   (10)_____

7 in the thousands place   (11)_____

8 in the tens place   (12)_____

0 in the ones place   (13)_____

3 in the hundreds place   (14)_____

ANSWER BOX

6534

3195

9007

7970

756

384

Reproduction restricted.

Placing commas in numbers is very helpful when reading long numbers. Commas are put between every group of **three place values**. Since every group of three places has a different name, a comma lets you know that a new group of higher value is beginning. Each place grouping always follows the HUNDREDS, TENS, and ONES pattern.

	hundreds	tens	(one)		hundreds	tens	ones
		thousands				**units**	
6,002 =	0	0	6,		0	0	2
40,198 =	0	4	0,		1	9	8
678,501 =	6	7	8,		5	0	1

☞ Place your commas in these long numerals. See if you can read them aloud to your teacher.

(1) 4629

(2) 50026

(3) 294761

(4) 723

(5) 829930

(6) 401987

(7) 20467

☞ Write the place value that contains the digit **7**. Place your comma in the longer numbers to help you.

(8) 4<u>7</u>02 =_____

(9) <u>7</u>398 =_____

(10) 56<u>7</u>1 =_____

(11) 2<u>7</u> =_____

(12) <u>7</u>013 =_____

(13) 90<u>7</u>20 =_____

(14) 645<u>7</u>0 =_____

(15) 82<u>7</u>046 =_____

Whole numbers can be written as long as you want them. Using four places (THOUSANDS, HUNDREDS, TENS, and ONES), you can write all the numbers up to 9,999. The first number that needs five places is 10,000. The TEN THOUSANDS place goes in front of the THOUSANDS.

Here are the place values for a five (5) place number. Again, the comma may be placed between the THOUSANDS place and the HUNDREDS place. Commas make the number much easier to read.

	THOUSANDS	UNITS
		tens (one)	*hundreds tens ones*
46,782=	4 6	7 8 2
30,040=	3 0	0 4 0
4,009=	0 4	0 0 9

☞ Read these number words. Then write the numerals. Don't forget **zero place holders** and **commas**.
  example: 2 thousands, 6 tens, 4 ones = 2,064

6 ten thousands, 4 thousands, 9 ones = (1)_____
5 thousands, 3 hundreds, 4 tens = (2)_____
9 ten thousands, 4 thousands, 2 hundreds, 4 tens = (3)_____
2 ten thousands, 2 hundreds, 2 ones = (4)_____
7 thousands, 8 ones = (5)_____
8 ten thousands, 5 thousands = (6)_____
6 thousands, 4 tens, 2 ones = (7)_____
9 ten thousands, 1 hundred, 3 tens = (8)_____
1 thousand, 2 hundreds, 7 ones = (9)_____
5 tens, 8 ones = (10)_____

☞ Write these numbers as words. Put in your commas for additional help.
  example: 4309 = <u>four thousand, three hundred nine</u>

(11) 2631 =_____

(12) 30095 =_____

(13) 780 =_____

(14) 80034=_____

(15) 26701 =_____

(16) 4006 =_____

☞ Write the name of the place where the digit is underlined.

    example: 43,<u>6</u>71 = <u>hundreds</u>

20,6<u>7</u>4 = _____(1)

<u>4</u>,228 = _____(2)

<u>6</u>3,004 = _____(3)

25,<u>9</u>12 = _____(4)

7<u>3</u>0 = _____(5)

74,98<u>0</u> = _____(6)

43,<u>1</u>50 = _____(7)

2<u>6</u>,397 = _____(8)

<u>6</u> = _____(9)

<u>9</u>0,472 = _____(10)

☞ Write these numbers with place value words. Put in your commas and <u>list your zeros</u>.

    example: 2,407 = <u>2 thousands, 4 hundreds, 0 tens, 7 ones</u>

(11) 3041 = _____

(12) 85 = _____

(13) 63209 = _____

(14) 178 = _____

(15) 10 = _____

(16) 2469 = _____

(17) 82109 = _____

(18) 3 = _____

(19) 607 = _____

(20) 40508 = _____

You know that numbers are never ending. You can write numbers as long as you wish, but it is helpful to be able to read them as well.

Here are the place values of larger numbers. Each place grouping increases in value as it moves to the left. The "--illion" numbers use Latin terms at the beginning of the word to help you know their order.

	trillions			billions			millions			thousands			units		
	hundreds	tens	(one)	hundreds	tens	(one)	hundreds	tens	(one)	hundreds	tens	(one)	hundreds	tens	ones
407,329,120 =	0	0	0,	0	0	0,	4	0	7,	3	2	9,	1	2	0
364,029,001,546 =	0	0	0,	3	6	4,	0	2	9,	0	0	1,	5	4	6
502,317,894,056,891 =	5	0	2,	3	1	7,	8	9	4,	0	5	6,	8	9	1

All of these numbers are much bigger than you will probably ever need to know. It is fun to play with big numbers, however. Did you notice the Latin "bi" in billion? A bicycle has 2 wheels (hence, the second "--illion".) How about the "tri" in trillion? A tricycle has 3 wheels (hence, the third "---illion").

☞ Put your commas in these long numbers. See if you can read them to your teacher.

(1) 2743091

(2) 39000400

(3) 6428971

(4) 309874256

(5) 9347500216

(6) 70421003902

(7) 2903574561

(8) 58204618

☞ Now write your own numbers using the digit 5 in the:

(9) tens place = _____

(10) ten thousands place = _____

(11) hundreds place = _____

(12) ones place = _____

In money, you not only have whole dollars, you also have cents. Between $0 and $1 are 99 little cents. None of those cents equals a dollar, but each cent is important. Cents can be added together and eventually make more whole dollars.

In our number system, an infinite number of **smaller parts of a whole** are also between <u>any two whole numbers</u>, just like the little cents. Each individual **smaller part** can be broken down into even smaller parts than you could ever imagine. All of these smaller parts can be written either as a **decimal number** or a fraction. This book will focus on the **decimal point** and **decimal numbers**.

If your number is less than 1, it is written without a whole number.

(ex: **0** .1 .2 .3 .4 .5 .6 .7 .8 .9 **1**)

If your number is more than 1, it is written with the **whole number** on the left, a **decimal point** (or dot) in the middle, and **decimal numbers** on the right. (ex: **2.4**, **35.96**, **1.8905**)

Read rule #1. You have seen this rule already in money. The decimal point separates the **whole dollars** from the **cents**. The whole dollars are to the left. The cents, or money that is less than a whole dollar, are to the right.

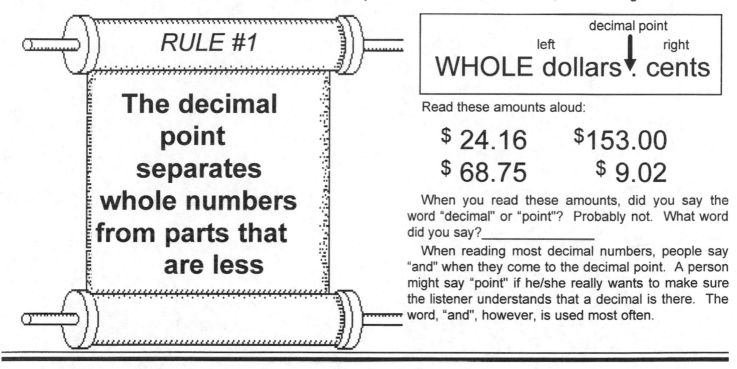

RULE #1

The decimal point separates whole numbers from parts that are less

decimal point
LEFT ↓ RIGHT
WHOLE numbers less than a whole

decimal point
left ↓ right
WHOLE dollars. cents

Read these amounts aloud:

$ 24.16 $153.00
$ 68.75 $ 9.02

When you read these amounts, did you say the word "decimal" or "point"? Probably not. What word did you say?_____

When reading most decimal numbers, people say "and" when they come to the decimal point. A person might say "point" if he/she really wants to make sure the listener understands that a decimal is there. The word, "and", however, is used most often.

☞ Write these money amounts as words. Be careful to use only one "and" for the decimal's place.

example: $ 310.40 = <u>three hundred ten dollars and forty cents</u>

(1) $26.58 = _____

(2) $416.04 = _____

(3) $3.08 = _____

(4) $6211.00 = _____

(5) $.69 = _____

(6) $12.05 = _____

RULE #2

Decimal numbers place values always end in the letters "TH".

Notice the slight differences in spelling and pronunciation of place values.

WHOLE NUMBERS	DECIMAL NUMBERS
ONES	----
TENS	TEN**TH**S
HUNDREDS	HUNDRED**TH**S
THOUSANDS	THOUSAND**TH**S
TEN THOUSANDS	TEN THOUSAND**TH**S

The ONES place is the only place *not* repeated on the decimal numbers side. There is no such thing as ONE-<u>TH</u>S. *All* multiples of 10 are repeated, but are spelled with a "**TH**".

These are how the place values look:

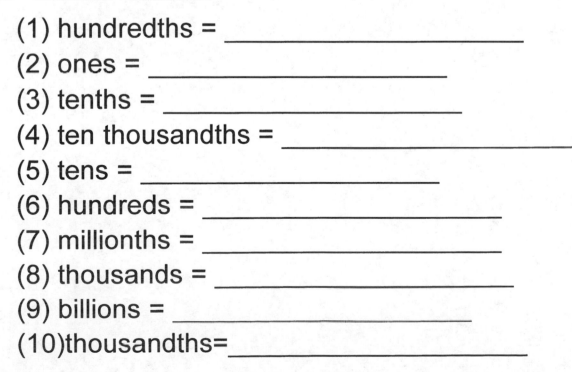

WHOLE NUMBERS → DECIMAL NUMBERS

ten thousands thousands hundreds tens ones . tenths hundredths thousandths ten thousandths

☞ Tell whether the following place values are <u>whole numbers</u> or <u>decimal numbers</u>.

example: **ten thousands = <u>whole number</u>**

(1) hundredths = _____

(2) ones = _____

(3) tenths = _____

(4) ten thousandths = _____

(5) tens = _____

(6) hundreds = _____

(7) millionths = _____

(8) thousands = _____

(9) billions = _____

(10) thousandths = _____

This is a whole box. It has been divided into **equal** parts. How many parts are in the box?_____ Each part is less than the whole box. But all of the parts are needed to make the whole. (Ten tenths equal one whole.)

Ten **equal** parts are called

TENTHS.

The tenths place is the **first** place value to the **right** of the decimal. They look like this:
.1 .2 .3 .4 .5 .6 .7 .8 .9

TENS ONES . *tenths*

In decimals, there is an easy way to figure out the place value name is you forget - pay attention to the number of zeros. For example: Tenths has to do with the number 10. Ten (10) has **one zero** in it. "One" is another name for **first**. Therefore, TENTHS is the **first place** in the decimal place values.

Here are some examples of tenths and how they are pronounced:

.7 = seven tenths

12.4 = twelve and four tenths

60.0 = sixty (there are **no** tenths)

☞ Write the following numbers in <u>words</u>. Use only <u>one "AND"</u> to mean the decimal.

example: 234.2 = <u>**two hundred thirty-four and two tenths**</u>

(1) 16.7 =_____

(2) .9 = _____

(3) 572.6 = _____

(4) 38.0 = _____

(5) 0.3 = _____

(6) 401.5 = _____

☞ Look at the number 4,386.9. What digit is in the following places:

tens = _____   ones = _____   tenths = _____

thousands = _____   hundreds = _____

The whole box has now been divided ten more times. If you counted every little square, you would come up with 100 (or the first 10 divisions times the second 10 divisions = 10x10=100). Notice how small the equal parts are now. They are ten times smaller than before. [One hundred hundredths equal one whole.]

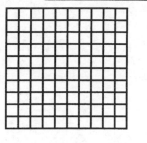

Each one of these one hundred **equal** parts is called a

HUNDREDTH.

1**00** has **2** zeros. "Two" = second.

HUNDREDTHS is the **2**nd decimal place value.

WHOLES .tenths   *hundredths*

They include all numbers between **.01** and **.99**

Here are some examples of **hundredths**:

.46 = forty-six hundredths

.05 = five hundredths

23.19 = twenty-three and nineteen hundredths

Do hundredths look familiar? They should. Hundredths are money without the dollar sign. It takes 100 cents to make a dollar. That makes each cent equal to ONE HUNDREDTH of a dollar. When you write money, you are actually saying:

$36.15= 36 dollars and 15 hundredths toward the next whole dollar.

You are saying the same thing with decimals - so many wholes and so much toward the next whole.

☞   Write the place value of the **underlined** digit.

example: 47.8**2** = **tenths**

(1) 63**2**.40 = _____

(2) **5**07.8 = _____

(3) 91.**7** = _____

(4) 92390.1**3** = _____

(5) **4**7203.68 = _____

(6) 53**2**.01 = _____

(7) 2690.**7**6 = _____

(8) 3**9**0456.25 = _____

(9) 6040.7**2** = _____

(10) 3**4**.65 = _____

(11) 1359.**0**3 = _____

(12) 46724.7**8** = _____

PAGE 19

☞ Write the following numbers in words.

1) 64.3 = _____

2) .04 = _____

3) 31.57 = _____

4) 247.19 = _____

5) 408.00 = _____

6) 8.56 = _____

7) 11.02 = _____

8) 600.40 = _____

9) 32,000.15 = _____

☞ Read these number words. Write the number on the line.

example: four hundred twenty and four tenths = <u>420.4</u>

10) two and forty-three hundredths   10)_____

11) thirty-seven and five hundredths   11)_____

12) six hundred fourteen and nine tenths   12)_____

13) nine thousand three hundred eight and

   fifty-three hundredths   13)_____

14) seventy-one thousand and six tenths   14)_____

15) eight hundredths   15)_____

16) one and one hundredth   16)_____

17) seven hundred   17)_____

18) seven hundredths   18)_____

19) five hundred four and three tenths   19)_____

20) sixteen and nine hundredths   20)_____

We can't draw the whole box and divide each hundredth square 10 more times. The spaces would be too small to see. Your next place value, **thousandths**, is quite small. If you measured one of the hairs on your head, it's width would measure about 3 thousandths of an inch. You would have to split that hair's width into 3 equal parts to see *one thousandth* of an inch. You also would need more than 330 hairs placed side by side to equal one inch.

We used commas in whole numbers to help us read them. **Never** use a comma in decimal numbers. A thousand has 3 zeros, so it will be the **third** place value to the right of the decimal. A thousand thousandths equal one whole.

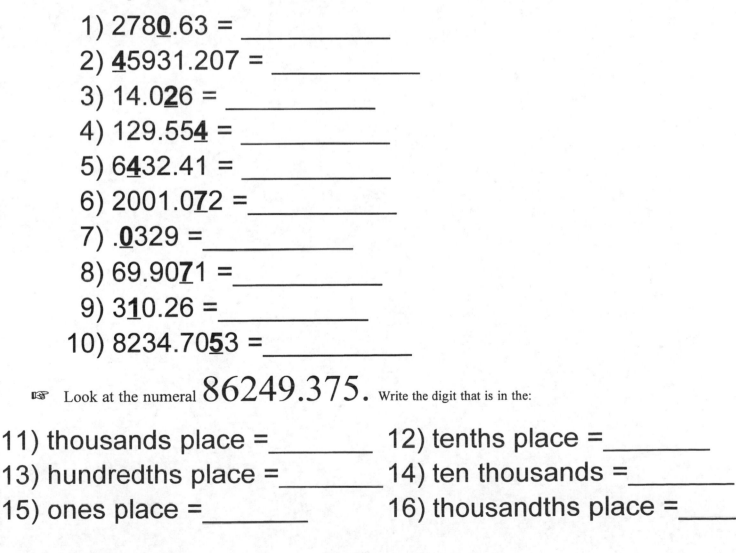

| WHOLES | | | | | decimals | | |
| THOUSANDS, | HUNDREDS | TENS | ONES | . | tenths | hundredths | *thousandths* |

All decimal numbers between *.001* and *.999* require the thousandths place. Here are some examples of **thousandths**:

   .470 = four hundred seventy thousandths

   .056 = fifty-six thousandths

   300.001 = three hundred point one thousandth (three hundred and one thousandth could be mistaken for .301 - using the word "point" makes it a bit clearer.)

☞ Write the place value of the **underlined** digit.

1) 2780.63 = _____

2) 45931.207 = _____

3) 14.026 = _____

4) 129.554 = _____

5) 6432.41 = _____

6) 2001.072 = _____

7) .0329 = _____

8) 69.9071 = _____

9) 310.26 = _____

10) 8234.7053 = _____

☞ Look at the numeral 86249.375. Write the digit that is in the:

11) thousands place = _____   12) tenths place = _____

13) hundredths place = _____   14) ten thousands = _____

15) ones place = _____   16) thousandths place = _____

☞ Write the place value of the digit 5.

1) 4650.237 = _____

2) 2394.512 = _____

3) 80.005 = _____

4) 75.267 = _____

5) 960.1534 = _____

☞ Read the number words. Write them as numerals.

fifty-three and two hundred four thousandths   6)_____

two thousand point twenty-four hundredths   7)_____

five thousandths   8)_____

two ten thousands, six ones and nine tenths   9)_____

five tens and eighteen thousandths   10)_____

nine thousands and seven tenths   11)_____

fifty-one dollars and seven cents   12)_____

sixty-three thousandths   13)_____

two tens, three ones, and four hundredths   14)_____

☞ Create your own numbers. They can be long or short. Put the digit 8 in the:

15) thousandths place = _____

16) tens place = _____

17) ten thousands place = _____

18) tenths place = _____

19) hundredths place = _____

20) thousands place = _____

The last place value you will use is TEN THOUSANDTHS. That is small enough. One TEN THOUSANDTH equals the width of a human hair split about 30 times (the world record is 17 times). (Ten thousand ten thousandths =1.) Remember that ten thousand (10,000) has **four zeros**, so ten thousandths will be the **fourth place** past the decimal.

WHOLES . ten<u>ths</u>   hundred<u>ths</u>   thousand<u>ths</u>   *ten thousand<u>ths</u>*

All decimal numbers between *.0001* and *.9999* require the ten thousandths place. **Ten thousandths** are read this way:

.0008 = eight ten thousandths
.0304 = three hundred four ten thousandths
6.0005 = six and five ten thousandths (or six "point" five ten thousandths)

☞   Look at the numbers in the answer box below. Which number has the digit:

6 in the tens place = (1)_____

9 in the hundredths place = (2)_____

5 in the ones place = (3)_____

0 in the tenths place = (4)_____

3 in the thousands place (5)_____

2 in the ten thousandths place = (6)_____

1 in the hundreds place = (7)_____

4 in the thousandths place = (8)_____

7 in the ten thousandths place = (9)_____

8 in the hundredths place = (10)_____

7 in the tenths place = (11)_____

6 in the ten thousandths place = (12)_____

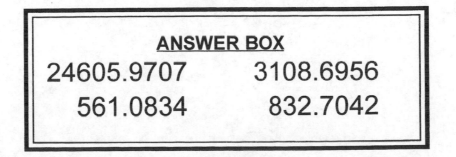

ANSWER BOX
24605.9707   3108.6956
561.0834   832.7042

Reproduction restricted.

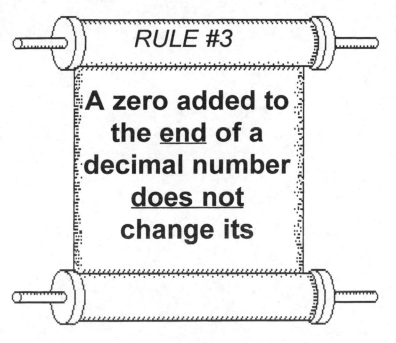

RULE #3

A zero added to the <u>end</u> of a decimal number <u>does not</u> change its

When you add a zero to the end of a whole number, you make it 10 times bigger. (ex: If you have a 10 and add a zero onto the end, the 10 becomes 100.) But when you have a decimal number and add a zero onto the end, you haven't changed its value at all.

Look at this example:

tenths   tenths hundredths

$$.4 = \quad .4 \quad 0$$

You added exactly zero hundredths to your answer. In other words, you added *nothing*.

> Think of it in terms of money. Tenths are dimes. Hundredths are pennies. Four dimes plus no pennies = $ .40. So, .4 = .40

So, whether your answer is .4, .40, or .400000000000, it still equals "four tenths" and is read "four tenths".

This **zero place holder** rule isn't meant to confuse you. Actually, it will help you in many ways. You will use it many times when working with decimals. Right now, you will use the zero place holder rule to compare decimal numbers of different sizes. On this page, you will find out which is the larger number. Here's how:

Which is larger?   .6 or .593

You have two numbers and you must find out which is larger. But one number is in tenths and the other number is in thousandths. Use your **zero place holder rule** on the numeral with the least number of places - add the right number of zeros to it so that **both** decimal numbers have the **same number of places**. Then it's easy to decide if a number is larger, smaller, or equal. Here's how to think it through:

Think: .6 =.600 and .593=.593

In whole numbers, 600 is more than 593

So, .6 is larger than .593

☞ Circle the larger number.

(1) .4 or .403

(2) .79 or .781

(3) .8 or .806

(4) .1046 or .146

(5) .23718 or .238

(6) .05 or .1

(7) .92 or .9199

(8) .843 or .8304

(9) .9999 or .99

(10) .4006 or .406

(11) .12 or .122

(12) .4782 or .472

(13) .63 or .603

(14) .3 or .4927

Reproduction restricted.

Using the **zero place holder rule** helps when your number contains both whole and decimal places.   Here is an example:

Which is larger? 16.2 or 16.289

In checking numbers which contain both wholes and decimals, always **check your wholes first**. If one whole number is larger, you have your answer. No matter how large the decimal number is, it can't make the wholes any larger. If the wholes are the same, then you must move to the decimal places to find out which is larger. Solve them the same as before. Make the decimal places of equal length and see which is larger.

> *Think:*   Is one whole number larger than the other? (NO)
>
>   .2=.200 compared to .289
>
>   200 is smaller than 289
>
>   So, 16.289 is the larger number

Have you noticed the ***shortcut*** yet? Start at the wholes and work down the number, from left to right, just like you read the number. Compare each place value. The **first** number that has a place worth more than the other is the larger.

The WHOLE numbers are the SAME. (Neither is larger so far.)

The *tenths* places are the SAME. (Neither is larger so far.)

The *hundredths* places show the first difference.

          .2 doesn't have a digit in its hundredths place.

          .289 has an *8* . *8* is more than nothing.

So, the number containing .289 (16.289) is larger.

☞ Compare these numerals. Circle the larger number.

(1) 1.32 or 1.3002   (2) 156.7 or 165.47

(3) 9.604 or 9.406   (4) 280.59 or 280.6

(5) 20.0048 or 20.01   (6) 3479.031 or 3479.30

☞ Compare these numerals. Circle the largest number.

(7) 19.76 or 19.678 or 19.876

(8) 36.5 or 36.57 or 35.76

(9) 74.02 or 74.0139 or 72.99

(10) 274.6721 or 247.7621 or 274.7

(11) 701.04 or 710.09 or 71.0106

Here is another way to use the rule: *A ZERO ADDED TO THE END OF A DECIMAL NUMBER DO NOT CHANGE ITS VALUE* - putting numbers in order.

Put these numbers in order from smallest to **largest**:

.57   .5   .572

Think: .57= .570   .5= .500   .572= .572

In whole numbers, 500 (.5) comes first, 570 (.57) next and 572 last. Therefore, the answer is .5, .57, .572

☞   Now its your turn. Put these numbers in order from **smallest** to **largest**::

1)   .63   .6   .607   (1)_____

2)   .7   .63   .72   (2)_____

3)   .1   1.   .01   (3)_____

4)   .47   .4   .347   (4)_____

5)   .68   .689   .6984   (5)_____

6)   .52   .532   .5237   (6)_____

7)   .602   .62   .612   (7)_____

8)   .19   .1869   .198   (8)_____

9)   .37   .3072   .3   (9)_____

10)   .409   .49   .4679   (10)_____

11)   .5212   .5   .521   (11)_____

12)   .234   .2043   .243   (12)_____

Reproduction restricted.

When the decimal contains whole numbers, **check the whole numbers first.** Then work out the decimals. Here is an example:

Put these numbers in order from smallest to **largest**.

14.3   13.67   13.602

Think: The two numbers with 13 wholes are less than the number with 14. The 13s will be smaller. The 14 will be largest.

For the 13s - .67= .670 and .602 = .602

602 is smaller than 670

So, <u>13.602 is smallest, 13.67 next and 14.3 will be largest.</u>

☞ Put these numbers in order from **smallest** to **largest**.

1)   15.4   15.04   15.404   (1)_____

2) 270.6   207.06   270.63   (2)_____

3) 72.5   52.7   25.7   (3)_____

4)   4.367   3.4   4.03   (4)_____

5) 603.0   306.0   030.6   (5)_____

6)   .09   .90   .009   (6)_____

7)   3.003   3.033   3.030   (7)_____

8) 473.02   473.2   437.002   (8)_____

9) 60.   .60   6.0   (9)_____

10) 52.67   52.7   52.6007   (10)_____

11) 83.09   82.901 83.809   (11)_____

Decimals make sense if you think about them in terms of money.

$10¢ = \$\ .10$ = dime = tenth = .1 = (10 tenths = 1 whole {dollar})

$25¢ = \$\ .25$ = quarter = .25 = (2 quarters = one half

and 4 quarters = 1 whole)

*$33¢ = \$\ .33$ = third (approximately) = (3 thirds = 1 whole)

$50¢ = \$\ .50$ = half = .5 = 2 quarters = (2 halves = 1 whole)

$75¢ = \$\ .75$ = three quarters = mid way between a half and a whole

$\$1.00$ = 100 cents = 1 whole and nothing extra

You remember that money is written in decimal notation to the hundredths place, a 2 digit place value. A dime ($\$\ .10$) could have been written (.1), but it needed a zero place holder to make it a two place number. The zero place holder at the end of a decimal doesn't change the decimal's value. A half ($\$\ .50$) also could have been written as (.5), but it also needed a zero place holder. Cents must have 2 places. Therefore, .1 and .5 must use a zero place holder to fill the hundredths place.

Remember the half especially. $.5$ is the dividing point for rounding off, a skill which you will learn in multiplication.

☞ Fill in the place value table below. All answers equal each other (all answers in the tenths row equal tenths, etc.). Do not write in the spaces containing (---).

	tenths	hundredths	thousandths	ten thousandths
tenth	1	10	100	
quarter	---	25		
*third	---	33	333	3333
half			500	
three quarters	---			7500
whole	10			

☞ Write the decimal numbers that equal each other. Each row is several ways to write the same number. Use zero place holders as needed to fill in the table below. Do not write in spaces containing (--).

	tenths	hundredths	thousandths	ten thousandths
.10	.1	.10	.100	.1000
.25	--	.25		
.33	--		.333	.3333
.50				
.75	--			
1.00	1.0			

*A third is a repeating decimal - it never ends and equals .3333333333333 forever!

There is another way to use decimals that saves reading a lot of zeros. Sometimes decimal numbers are combined with words. This saves space and makes the number easier to read, For example:

4.6 thousand is easier to read than 4,600.

3.5 million is easier to read than 3,500,000.

16.3 billion is easier to read than 16,300,000,000.

Look for a pattern in the examples above. To write the words out as numbers, you must know what to do with the decimal point and where to put your commas. Did you notice that the decimal point became a comma? Then you just filled in each number with the right amount of zero place holders to make it correct.

It is helpful to remember how many places each number has. Maybe you can remember them like this:

thousands = 1 comma and 3 places = number,000

millions = 2 commas and 6 places = number,000,000

billions = 3 commas and 9 places = number,000,000,000

☞ Write these words as numbers. All facts taken from Guiness Book of World Records, 1989 Edition.

1. N.C. led the nation in turkey production with 50.1 million in 1989. They grew _____ turkeys.

2. In 1982, there were approximately 6.5 billion chickens in the world. The _____ chickens would equal 1.4 chickens for every person on earth today.

3. *Chi-Lin*, a panda in the Madrid Zoo, Spain is worth $1.2 million. Her price tag would look like _____.

4. The greatest price paid for a used car was $9.485 million. The 1931 Bugatti Royale (one of six made) cost_____.

5. R. L. Bender drove his car 1.02 million miles from 1958-83. That would be _____ mile used car!

6. The most accurate clock only loses one second every 1.7 million years. That's not much time in _____ years.

7. The highest auction price ever paid for a carousel animal was $35.2 thousand. That tiger cost _____.

Reproduction restricted.

☞ Now write these numbers as words. All facts from Guinness Book of World Records, 1989 Edition.

1. The caterpillar crawler that carried the *Saturn V* rockets to the launch pad cost $12,300,000 to build. The price tag of _____ should be doubled because 2 were built.

2. The largest power shovel in the world weighs 24,250,000 lbs. The _____ shovel needs 20 electric motors to operate its 220.5 ft.-long boom arm.

3. The largest antique ever sold was the London Bridge for $2,460,000. The _____ bridge was then brought to Arizona and rebuilt, at a cost of $6,900,000. That's another _____ for 10,000 tons of stone.

4. The highest price ever paid for a fountain pen was $2,340,000. The _____ pen had 600 jewels on it.

5. The highest price paid for a post card was $4,400. The _____ card was one of only five known in the world.

6. A Rome, Italy, dentist saved nearly 2,001,000 teeth. He pulled these _____ teeth at an average of 185 a day.

7. The most expensive wallet ever made cost $72,000. The _____ wallet was diamond-studded crocodile.

8. The world's population in 1986 was 4,917,000,000 people. By the 2100AD, our _____ people are expected to increase to 10,500,000,000. That's _____ people.

9. Life Savers, between 1913-87, sold about 33,430,000,000 rolls. The _____ candies, put hole to hole, would stretch to the moon and back more than 3 times!

You have worked with place value and should be comfortable with both whole numbers and decimals. Now, let's put that knowledge to work for you. It's time to learn addition, using both whole numbers and decimals.

You have been using the rule for addition of decimals without realizing it. When you added money problems, they contained decimals. This was the rule you followed:

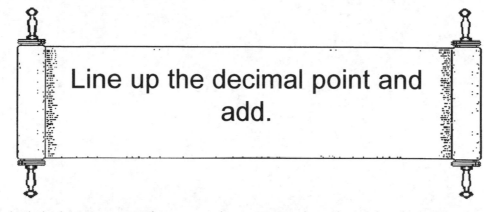

Line up the decimal point and add.

Pretty easy, right? Let's look at two examples - one using money and one just using decimals.

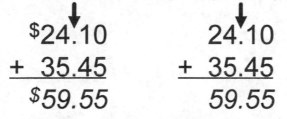

$$\begin{array}{r} \$24.10 \\ +\ 35.45 \\ \hline \$59.55 \end{array} \qquad \begin{array}{r} 24.10 \\ +\ 35.45 \\ \hline 59.55 \end{array}$$

Find your decimal points. They are lined up **directly below each other**. When the decimals line up, the digits in each place value line up (the wholes line up, the tenths line up, and the hundredths line up).

In both problems, you started at the right side of the problem and worked left (just like a regular addition problem). You added the decimal places together first and the whole number places last (just like a regular money problem).

In both problems, you brought your decimal point straight down. This separated your wholes from the decimal numbers (which were less than one whole). Without the decimal point, your answer would be wrong.

The only difference between the two problems is the dollar sign. If you forget the dollar sign in your money problem answer, your answer is wrong. If you put a dollar sign in the problem where one is not needed, your answer is wrong.

☞ Add these numbers.

$$\begin{array}{r} 46.2 \\ +\ 32.5 \end{array} \qquad \begin{array}{r} 10.57 \\ +\ 29.21 \end{array} \qquad \begin{array}{r} 61.953 \\ +\ 38.023 \end{array} \qquad \begin{array}{r} 1.0281 \\ +\ 7.9106 \end{array}$$

$$\begin{array}{r} \$703.63 \\ +\ 251.05 \end{array} \qquad \begin{array}{r} 2.395 \\ +\ 4.203 \end{array} \qquad \begin{array}{r} .46 \\ +\ .42 \end{array} \qquad \begin{array}{r} 80.101 \\ +\ 14.325 \end{array}$$

Line up the decimal point and add.

37.02 + 42.65	20.381 + 27.406	6.5 + 8.2	2.7321 + 9.0527
.7092 + .1006	$395.75 + 780.12	41.36 + 69.43	89.007 + 19.991
.4 + .3	82.047 + 63.922	6.3092 + 7.5805	910.33 + 278.54
89.031 + 62.937	64.7 + 88.1	$250.08 + 865.70	3.7706 + 7.0192
57.1 63.4 + 17.3	3.092 1.903 + 9.001	.4272 .1302 + .3313	$88.25 27.10 + 75.43

Reproduction restricted.

PERFECTING THE POINT   ADDITION   NAME_____

DATE_____

When you added money problems, you had no difficulty with regrouping (carrying). Solve this sample problem:

$$\begin{array}{r} \$25.40 \\ +\ 41.73 \\ \hline \end{array}$$

When the cents' side became more than 100, you regrouped (carried) the 1 to the whole dollar's side. You didn't pay attention to the decimal point until you brought it straight down and wrote it into your answer.

Problems containing decimal points, but no dollar signs, work the same way. Look at these examples:

$$\begin{array}{r} \overset{1}{4}.9 \\ +\ 1.6 \\ \hline \end{array} \qquad \begin{array}{r} 5\overset{1}{2}.39 \\ +\ 14.80 \\ \hline \end{array} \qquad \begin{array}{r} \overset{1\ 1}{6}.429 \\ +\ 7.926 \\ \hline \end{array} \qquad \begin{array}{r} \overset{1\ \ 1\ \ 1}{34}.8946 \\ +\ 21.2437 \\ \hline \end{array}$$

☞ Solve these problems. Remember to regroup (carry) whenever it is needed.

$$\begin{array}{r} 49.7 \\ +\ 77.6 \\ \hline \end{array} \qquad \begin{array}{r} 64.83 \\ +\ 58.42 \\ \hline \end{array} \qquad \begin{array}{r} 24.708 \\ +\ 86.525 \\ \hline \end{array} \qquad \begin{array}{r} .4783 \\ +\ .6021 \\ \hline \end{array}$$

$$\begin{array}{r} \$325.85 \\ +\ 409.25 \\ \hline \end{array} \qquad \begin{array}{r} 83.9 \\ +\ 17.6 \\ \hline \end{array} \qquad \begin{array}{r} 9.276 \\ +\ 8.805 \\ \hline \end{array} \qquad \begin{array}{r} 5.5594 \\ +\ 9.2407 \\ \hline \end{array}$$

$$\begin{array}{r} 58.859 \\ +\ 60.730 \\ \hline \end{array} \qquad \begin{array}{r} .9337 \\ +\ .2001 \\ \hline \end{array} \qquad \begin{array}{r} 2.76 \\ +\ 7.13 \\ \hline \end{array} \qquad \begin{array}{r} .8 \\ +\ .9 \\ \hline \end{array}$$

$$\begin{array}{r} 47.523 \\ 50.602 \\ +\ 15.607 \\ \hline \end{array} \qquad \begin{array}{r} 6.9802 \\ 8.0239 \\ +\ 2.0406 \\ \hline \end{array} \qquad \begin{array}{r} \$27.93 \\ 41.05 \\ +\ 55.02 \\ \hline \end{array} \qquad \begin{array}{r} 267.8 \\ 329.6 \\ +\ 700.3 \\ \hline \end{array}$$

Reproduction restricted.

If you follow the rule for adding decimals, you will have no difficulty in solving a problem like this:

$$42.23 + 25.14 = ?$$

The rule says:

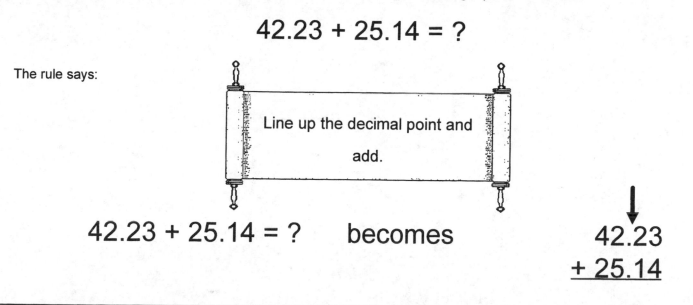

Line up the decimal point and add.

$$42.23 + 25.14 = ?\quad\text{becomes}\quad\begin{array}{r}42.23\\+\ 25.14\\\hline\end{array}$$

☞ Write your vertical problem in the space next to the printed horizontal problem.

(1) 63.9 + 27.8 =

(2) 2.984 + 3.075 =

(3) 29.0307 + 46.9923 =

(4) $525.95 + 375.05 =

(5) 380.27 + 627.85 =

(6) 14.8036 + 65.7248 =

(7) 463.9702 + 207.0389 + 120.2537 =

```
    7.9          4.8          2.9 + 3.7 =
  + 8.5        + 5.2
```

```
    6.798       12.365       $4.75 + 9.80 =
  + 5.722      + 89.203
```

```
  $267.58       9.2783       5.398 + 2.305 =
  + 508.26     + 8.7302
```

```
    8.4         76.809        4.3 + 8.7 + 6.4 =
    3.3         94.216
  + 9.8        + 17.302
```

```
   68.7        $27.45        7.3 + 6.8 + 2.1 + 5.5 =
   20.0         10.09
   16.2         42.61
  + 30.5       + 38.95
```

6.47 + 9.21 + 2.06 + 1.38 + 7.75 =

Suppose you need to add whole numbers of different lengths. Use the decimal addition rule:

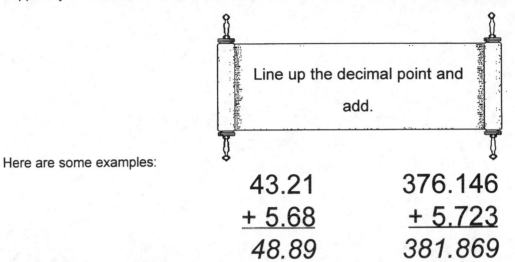

Line up the decimal point and add.

Here are some examples:

$$43.21$$
$$+ \ 5.68$$
$$48.89$$

$$376.146$$
$$+ \ 5.723$$
$$381.869$$

If you want to keep your number columns very straight, you also might like to use your **zero place holder rule** for whole numbers. At the **beginning** of a whole number, you may write as many zeros as you need without changing the number's value. Your sample problems would then look like this:

$$43.21$$
$$+ \ \textit{0} \ 5.68$$
$$48.89$$

$$376.146$$
$$+ \ \textit{00} \ 5.723$$
$$381.869$$

Use the way which is best for you.

═══

$$2.16$$
$$+ \ 64.27$$

$$4.917$$
$$+ \ 28.315$$

$$720.6$$
$$+ \ 1.8$$

$$3.9921$$
$$+ \ 40.1519$$

$$554.9$$
$$+ \ 2.8$$

$$367.01$$
$$+ \ 14.93$$

$$9.1407$$
$$+ \ 68.2225$$

$$8.693$$
$$+ \ 436.257$$

$$3.4$$
$$267.5$$
$$+ \ 50.3$$

$$20.3719$$
$$1.9024$$
$$+ \ 374.8201$$

$$6.25$$
$$184.32$$
$$+ \ 62.08$$

$$529.873$$
$$.637$$
$$+ \ 41.202$$

Suppose you need to add decimal numbers of different lengths. Use the decimal addition rule:

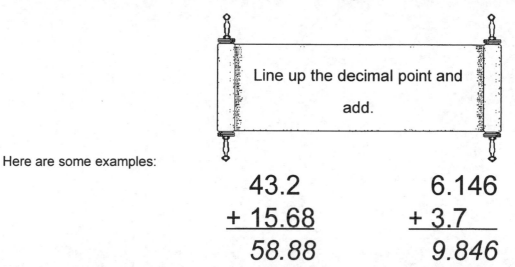

Line up the decimal point and add.

Here are some examples:

```
  43.2          6.146
+ 15.68        + 3.7
  58.88          9.846
```

If you want to keep your number columns very straight, you also might like to use your **zero place holder rule** for decimals. At the **end** of a decimal number, you may write as many zeros as you need without changing the number's value. Your sample problems would then look like this:

```
  43.20          6.146
+ 15.68        + 3.700
  58.88          9.846
```

Use the way which is best for you.

```
  43.67        90.5          3.7209        1.924
+ 57.5       + 32.735      + 28.6        + 8.6785
```

```
  307.8          .4761       $80.85        73.045
+ 625.94       + .36        + 29.65      + 16.99
```

```
  600.47        5.9205        3.7          7.884
+ 600.9       + 8.091       + 8.9236     + 3.1897
```

    Reproduction restricted.

$$4.31 + 79.0124$$

$$\$733.02 + 6.98$$

$$59.0064 + 8.04$$

$$78.1037 + 19.7$$

$$607.25 + 9.8$$

$$5.2227 + 92.87$$

$$810.09 + 9.9143$$

$$.6892 + 374.67$$

$$8.993 + 27.01 + 486.7$$

$$8.1029 + 17.2 + 3.998$$

$$2.46 + .957 + 65.3906$$

$$830.55 + 76.3 + .9823$$

$4.9 + .395 =$

$7.2907 + 83.6 =$

$390.8 + 2.439 =$

$57.258 + 925.9 =$

$68.023 + 8.0075 + .6 =$

$.7 + 5.75 + 86.3049 =$

$7.68 + 1.8203 + .5 + 30.721 =$

$206.478 + .2 + 3.67 + 40.5 =$

(1) Mark's team had 4 runners for the 100 yd. dash. Their times were 10.3, 10.21, 10.42, and 10.7 seconds. What was the total time for Mark's team?_____

(2) Jerry's team also ran the 100 yd. dash. Their times were 10.4, 10.2, 10.6, and 10.38. What was the total time? _____ Which was the fastest time on Jerry's team?_____

3) Which team won - Mark's or Jerry's?_____
What was the best time for both teams?_____
Which was the slowest?_____

(4) Laura's team swam the 50 meter butterfly. Their times were 34.3, 32.68, 33.93, and 34.02 seconds. What was their total time?_____ What was the fastest time on the team?_____

(5) Ashley's team swam the butterfly in 32.7, 33.59, 34.4 and 33.98 seconds. What was their total time?_____
What was the slowest time on the team?_____

(6) Which team won - Laura's or Ashley's?_____

(7) Myra's team ran the 200 meters in 26.8, 27.32, 27.83, and 27.55 seconds. What was their total time?_____
What was the slowest time on the team?_____

(8) Maggie's team ran the 200 meters in 27.4, 26.92, 27.54, and 27.49 seconds. What was their total time?_____

(9) Who's team won - Myra's or Maggie's?_____
What was the best time for both teams?_____

When you must add a whole number (with no decimal places) to a number containing decimal places, how do you do it?

Look at the whole number   **63**   Does it have a decimal point?_____

If it did, where would the decimal point be? Write the decimal point in the correct place on the 63 above.

Whole numbers have an "understood decimal point". You "understand" (or know) where the decimal point should be, even though it isn't written there. Since you know where it should be, you can write a decimal point without hurting a thing. This decimal point you write at the end of the whole number will give you the necessary point to **line up and add**. Then you will be adding the whole numbers only with the whole numbers and the decimal numbers only with the decimal numbers. Here is an example:

$$72 + 6.43 = \qquad \begin{array}{r} 72. \\ + \ 6.43 \\ \hline \end{array}$$

---

(1) 29.316 + 4 =

(2) 367 + 82.9934 =

(3) 72.6 + 5 + 180.638 =

(4) 78 + 102.3 + 3 =

(5) 83.0402 + 6.9 + 510 =

(6) 35 + .8735 + 24.7 + 103 =

(7) 186.4 + 3 + .759 =

(8) 64 + .64 + 6.4 + .064 =

(9) 39.7 + 24.571 + .42 + 237 =

(10) 604 + 3.251 + .98 + 6 + .1 =

1. The largest ice cream sundae made in Canada (1988) used 44,689.5 lb. of ice cream, 9,688.1 lb. of syrup, and 537.2 lb. of topping. How much did it weigh?_____

2. The largest milk shake contained 117.5 gal. of vanilla ice cream, 60 gal. of milk, and 17 gal. of strawberry flavoring. How many gallons were in the final milk shake?_____

3. The largest meat pie ever baked contained 2,000 lb. of crust and 11,362.9 lb. of filling. What did the "Chuck Wagon Gang's Chili Meat Pie" weigh?_____

4. The largest pecan pie contained 1,059.5 lb. of pecans and 12,403.5 lb. of other ingredients. How much did the Oklahoma State University's pie weigh?_____

5. The largest U.S. ice cream sundae contained 26,020 lb. of ice cream, 7,521.75 lb. of topping, and 75 lb. of whipped cream. Fork lifts and ladders were needed to stack this _____, 30-million-calorie sundae.

6. In 1987, the U.S. mailed more mail than anywhere else in the world. People sent 78.9 billion first class and 75 billion packages and other class mail. How many letters and packages were mailed?_____

7. HM Cruiser *Edinburgh* was sunk in 1942, carrying 460 gold ingots. The gold was salvaged in 1981 and split among 3 groups. The USSR got $26.3 million, Great Britain got $13.15 million, and the salvage contractors got $32.4 million. How much was recovered?_____

In addition, you started out with a certain amount and ended up with more. In subtraction, you start out with and amount and end up with **less**. Addition and subtraction are opposites.

In subtraction, you are looking for the **difference** between two numbers. Your answer in subtraction is called the **difference**. Even though addition and subtraction are opposites, their decimal rules are very similar.

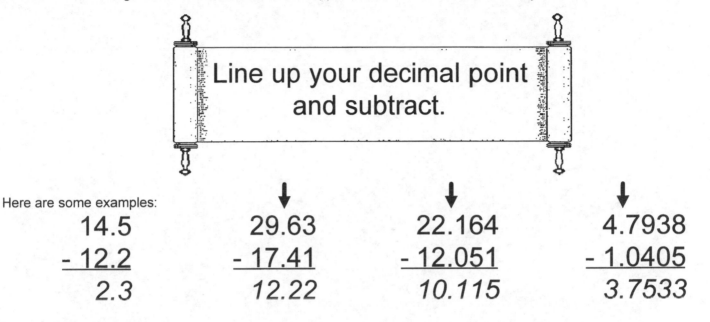

Here are some examples:

14.5	29.63	22.164	4.7938
- 12.2	- 17.41	- 12.051	- 1.0405
2.3	12.22	10.115	3.7533

Don't forget the most important part - **put you decimal in your answer** by **bringing it straight down.**

2.394	45.53	$85.96	.9
- 1.251	- 22.31	- 60.84	- .7

77.59	428.3	2.65	5.4378
- 35.27	- 103.1	- 1.23	- 1.2074

$405.39	6.2004	86.7	999.278
- 204.25	- 3.1001	- 70.5	- 846.107

23.8945 - 10.7442 =   745.278 - 405.203 =

As in subtraction with money problems, you borrow (regroup) wherever and whenever necessary. Once you've lined up your problem, you can forget about the decimal point until it is time to put it into your answer. Some people write their decimal point in their answer space even before they start working their problem. This helps them never to forget the important little point in their answer.

Here are some examples:

$$
\begin{array}{r}
\$53.07 \\
-\ 20.49 \\
\hline
\$32.58
\end{array}
\qquad
\begin{array}{r}
53.07 \\
-\ 20.49 \\
\hline
32.58
\end{array}
\qquad
\begin{array}{r}
\$19.27 \\
-\ 8.48 \\
\hline
\$10.79
\end{array}
\qquad
\begin{array}{r}
19.27 \\
-\ 8.48 \\
\hline
10.79
\end{array}
$$

Solve your problems, making sure to bring that all important little **decimal point straight down into your answer**. Don't forget your dollar sign if one is needed. That's all there is to it.

☞   Find the difference. Regroup when necessary.

$$
\begin{array}{r}
7.328 \\
-\ 4.609 \\
\hline
\end{array}
\qquad
\begin{array}{r}
9.3047 \\
-\ 4.3806 \\
\hline
\end{array}
\qquad
\begin{array}{r}
.28 \\
-\ .09 \\
\hline
\end{array}
\qquad
\begin{array}{r}
90.6 \\
-\ 29.8 \\
\hline
\end{array}
$$

$$
\begin{array}{r}
.3905 \\
-\ .1914 \\
\hline
\end{array}
\qquad
\begin{array}{r}
57.176 \\
-\ 28.085 \\
\hline
\end{array}
\qquad
\begin{array}{r}
\$38.00 \\
-\ 19.25 \\
\hline
\end{array}
\qquad
\begin{array}{r}
4628.5 \\
-\ 3282.7 \\
\hline
\end{array}
$$

72.046 - 50.802 = $504.75 - 238.90 =

67.0359 - 50.2079 =   53.047 - 46.149 =

345.006 - 250.018 =   50.2007 - 16.0430 =

Because subtraction is the opposite of addition, you will use addition to check your subtraction problems. Here are two examples.

2.435 minuend	→	1.204
- 1.204 subtrahend	→	+ 1.231
1.231 difference		2.435

4.086	→	2.619
- 2.619	→	+ 1.467
1.467		4.086

In subtraction, you start with a certain amount (your top number or **minuend**). From this amount, you take some of it away (the "take away" second number or **subtrahend**) and end up with less (your answer which is the **difference**). When you check with addition, you add the number you took away to your subtraction answer (the **difference**). If your addition answer equals the number you started with in your subtraction problem (the top number or **minuend**), your subtraction answer (the **difference**) is correct. If your addition answer does not equal the top number of your subtraction problem, you have a mistake somewhere and better try again.

☞ Find the difference. Check any 12 problems.

| 46.9 | 22.65 | .9420 | 8.002 |
| - 18.7 | - 18.93 | - .6481 | - 6.091 |

| 520.65 | 7.047 | 20.115 | 3.0902 |
| - 260.81 | - 4.128 | - 14.021 | - 2.0604 |

| $90.75 | 74.012 | .3124 | 5.4 |
| - 27.89 | - 26.121 | - .2016 | - 3.8 |

64.0392 - 46.0502 =   93.148 - 64.009 =

Remember your **zero place holder rules**? They are just as helpful in subtraction as they were in addition.

WHOLE NUMBER RULE		DECIMAL NUMBER RULE	
29.3 minuend 29.3		43.6 43.600	
$-\ 8.2$ subtrahend $-\ 0\ 8.2$		$-\ 21.849$ $-\ 21.549$	
21.1 difference		22.051	

Line up your decimal points. Then, to make sure both the top number (minuend) and bottom number (subtrahend) have the same number of places, add the correct number of **zero place holders**. Now you can find the **difference** easily.

As you can see, you must be very good at borrowing (or regrouping) with zeros when you subtract. This is the hardest skill to master in subtraction. Always regroup whenever and wherever necessary.

☞ Find the difference. Check any 10 problems.

$$
\begin{array}{r} 83.27 \\ -\ 6.3 \\ \hline \end{array}
\qquad
\begin{array}{r} 2.904 \\ -\ .17 \\ \hline \end{array}
\qquad
\begin{array}{r} .7 \\ -\ .346 \\ \hline \end{array}
\qquad
\begin{array}{r} 40.9401 \\ -\ 5.48 \\ \hline \end{array}
$$

$$
\begin{array}{r} 4.006 \\ -\ .1005 \\ \hline \end{array}
\qquad
\begin{array}{r} 3.29 \\ -\ 1.1023 \\ \hline \end{array}
\qquad
\begin{array}{r} 10.8 \\ -\ 5.0001 \\ \hline \end{array}
\qquad
\begin{array}{r} 30.7753 \\ -\ 3.8 \\ \hline \end{array}
$$

$57.9 - 12.64 =$ $98.56 - 89.4 =$

$70.004 - .9 =$ $54.8 - 5.468 =$

$\$93.05 - 8.95 =$ $.9 - .1234 =$

How do you subtract a number containing decimals from a whole number with no decimal places? The same way as in addition - place your decimal point and use **zero place holders**.

$$25 - 3.24 = \qquad \begin{array}{r} 25.00 \\ -\ 3.24 \\ \hline 21.76 \end{array}$$

☞ Find the difference. Check any 8 problems.

10 - 3.6 =   81 - 4.17 =

156 - 8.0104 =   38 - .406 =

895 - 37.02 =   70 - 2.009 =

53.4 - 29.315 =   673 - 4.55 =

318 - 84.87 =   7 - .4296 =

1) Mary and Joy ran the 100 yd. dash. Mary's time was 10.4 seconds. Joy's time was 10.38 seconds. Who won the race?_____ How much did she win by?_____

2) Jeremy and Barry ran the 400 meter race. Jeremy ran it in 50.4 seconds. Barry ran it in 50.56 seconds. Who won?_____ By how much?_____

3) Three horses are tied for the world's speed record in a half mile race. They averaged 40.54 mph. The horse holding the mile race's speed record ran it in 39.21 mph. What was the difference in their speeds?_____

4) The fastest speed for a male downhill skier (snow) was 139.030 mph. The fastest woman's downhill speed was 133.234 mph. What was the difference?_____

5) Matt Biondi (US) broke the 100 meter freestyle swimming world record three times in 1985-86. He shortened his time from 49.36 sec. to 48.74 sec. How much did he improve?_____

6) The fastest freestyle speed for a man in the 50 meter swim was 22.18 seconds. The fastest woman swam it in 24.98 seconds. Who was the fastest?_____ What was the difference in their times?_____

7) The fastest male 100 meter race was run in 9.83 seconds. The fastest female 100 meter race was run in 10.49 seconds. What was the difference in their times?_____

All record times taken from Guinness Book of World Records, 1989 edition.

There are some **shortcuts** in subtraction. One is in **checking subtraction problems** with addition. It can get boring rewriting your problem all over again. Here is a quick way to check with **no rewriting**.

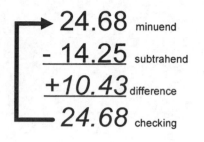

24.68 minuend
- 14.25 subtrahend
+10.43 difference
24.68 checking

sum

Solve your problem as usual, lining up your decimal points and subtracting the subtrahend from the minuend. Add your answer (the **difference**) to the subtrahend (the number just above your answer). This sum should be the same as your top number (the **minuend**). If they are equal, your subtraction answer is correct! If they aren't, check your subtraction answer (the **difference**) first and, if necessary, your addition.

☞ Find the difference. Check any 10 problems.

$$92.04 - 4.3$$

$$18.7 - 4.15$$

$$64.275 - 20.8$$

$$.8 - .3729$$

$$76.5 - 8.637$$

$$20.13 - 12.9$$

$$\$75.00 - 28.50$$

$$.9041 - .04$$

$$59.06 - 27.5 =$$

$$96.2 - .4387 =$$

$$8.604 - .3806 =$$

$$47.9 - 40.009 =$$

$$78.02 - 35.8 =$$

$$49.05 - 39.6471 =$$

America is a country which allows you to enter any business field you want. You may start any kind of company you wish, so long as you have the money needed to run it.

Sometimes, people have a company already started but need additional money to grow bigger. If they are a good, reliable company, there are several ways they can get the money. One way is to borrow it from a bank. They must pay the bank back in full, plus some additional money, called interest. This is very expensive for big companies.

Another way, if the company is big enough, is to join the STOCK MARKET. They sell SHARES of their company to people. The company promises to pay the SHAREHOLDERS money **if** the company makes a profit. If the company makes money, the stock's worth goes up. If the company loses money, the stock's worth goes down.

Shareholders take a chance with their investment. They hope to make more money than they spent to buy the stock. People can buy and sell their stock at any time. People try to buy stock when they think it is cheapest and try to sell when they think it is worth the most. Sometimes, shareholders are right in their buying and selling times, and make a profit. Sometimes they are wrong, and lose money.

The DOW JONES INDUSTRIAL AVERAGE is one measurement of stock price movement on the stock market for many companies. Everyday, the "Dow" has a CLOSING AVERAGE. This can be UP or DOWN from the day before. If it is UP, more companies made money than lost money. If it is DOWN, more companies lost money. People watch this up and down movement on the television news and/or in the newspaper. This movement shows approximately how strong our economy is.

☞   Solve these problems. When stocks go **UP** - add (because stocks become worth **more**). When stocks go **DOWN** - subtract (because stocks become worth **less**).

1. The Dow began the day at the 2478.4 level. It closed UP 37.6. What is the new average?_____

2. The Dow began the day at the 2553.2 level. It closed DOWN 14.86. What is the new average?_____

3. The Dow began the day at the 2592.61 level. It closed DOWN 27.73. What was the closing average?_____

4. The Dow began the day at the 2493.7 level. It closed UP 36.94. What was the closing average?_____

5. The Dow began the day at the 2643 level. It closed DOWN 9.58. What was the closing average?_____

6. The Dow began the day at the 2578.14 level. It closed DOWN 1.93. What was the closing average?_____

7. The Dow began the day at the 2596 level. It closed UP 27.16. What was the closing average?_____

Another **shortcut** is working with horizontal problems. You don't need to rewrite the whole problem, just part of it.

$$29.47 - 14.25 =$$
$$- \ 14.25 \quad \longleftarrow$$
$$15.22$$

═══

☞ Find the difference. Use the shortcut method. Check any 7 problems.

$32.4 - 17.645 =$ $51 - 3.492 =$

$64.73 - 8.6 =$ $246.1 - 81.94 =$

$57 - 6.041 =$ $39.576 - 16.41 =$

$10 - .001 =$ $83.9 - 25.6567 =$

$45.3492 - 8 =$ $903.224 - 80.008 =$

October 13, 1989, was the date of the worst one day plunge in stock market history. The Dow Jones Industrial Average lost more points in one day than ever before.

1. The Dow fell 190.58, closing at the 2569.26 level. What was the STARTING average?_____

2. On Monday, Oct. 16, the Dow started at Friday's closing 2569.26 level. In the first 40 min., it dropped another 63.52 points. What was the new low?_____

3. Then the Dow began to climb. From its starting level (2569.26), it gained 88.12 points by closing time. What was Monday's closing average?_____

4. Tuesday morning, stocks opened at Monday's (#3) closing average and plunged 60.25 points. What was the morning low?_____

5. Wednesday morning, the market opened at Tuesday's closing 2638.73 level. The Dow closed up 4.92. What was Wednesday's closing average?_____

6. Wed.'s closing (#5) was Thurs.'s opening average. The Dow closed up 39.55. Thurs. closing average?_____

7. Friday, stocks closed with a gain of 5.94 points. What was the new closing average? (#6)_____

8. During the week, the Dow closed up 88.12 (Mon.), down 18.65 (Tues.), up 4.92 (Wed.), up 39.55 (Thurs.), and up 5.94 (Fri.). What was the record weekly gain?_____

All information taken from the Wall Street Journal, Oct. 16-23, 1989
Dow Jones Co., Inc.

When checking subtraction problems, you add. When checking addition problems, you must subtract.

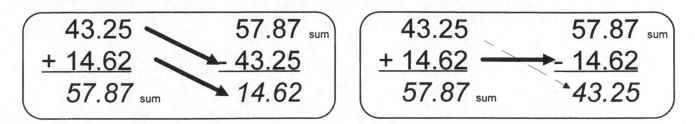

Since it took both numbers to make the **sum**, you can subtract either one to check the problem. Take your choice. Just make sure the **difference** in the subtraction check is the other number - the one you didn't choose.

☞ Find the sum. Check any 10 problems.

4.3702	3.56	29.817	.6
+ 19.29	+ 7.4089	+ 6.524	+ .93

6.4 + 87.553 =   48.963 + 3.0481 =

90.1 + 62.935 =   8.4615 + 3 =

47.9002 + 60.19 = $75.83 + 125.17 =

27.047 + 15.09 =   46 + 18.3576 =

95.6 + .9328 =   84.95 + 278.3 =

Reproduction restricted.

The first successful gasoline-powered car was built in Germany and ran about 8-10 mph. Today, these are the fastest cars in their class and their official record speeds.

jet-engine	633.468 mph	rocket-engine	622.287 mph
diesel	203.3 mph	turbine	429.311 mph
multi-piston	418.504 mph	single-piston	357.391 mph

Compared to these, the fastest turtle "ran" .23 mph.

1. What was the fastest type of car?_____ Slowest?_____

2. What was the difference in their speeds?_____

3. The turbine wheel-driven engine was how much faster than the multi-piston wheel driven engine?_____

4. The turbine engine was how much faster than the single-piston?_____

5. Compared to a turtle, how much faster was the diesel?_____

6. Compared to the fastest speed of the first gasoline car, how much slower was the turtle?_____

7. What was the speed difference between the jet and rocket-engine?_____

The slowest animals on earth include:

three-toed sloth	.068-.098 mph (6-8 ft. per minute)
three-toed sloth (fastest pace)	.170 mph (up to 15 ft./min.)
garden snail	.03 mph
giant tortoise	.17 mph
sea otter	6 mph

The fastest insect, a cockroach, can move 2.90 mph.

8. Which is the "fastest" of the slowest animals?_____

9. Which is the slowest animal?_____

10. What is the difference between the sloth's slowest and fastest speeds?_____

11. Compared to the sea otter, the giant tortoise moves how much slower?_____

12. Compared to the garden snail, the sea otter goes how much faster?_____

13. The cockroach moves _____ slower than the otter.

14. The sloth's fastest pace is _____ slower than the cockroach.

15. Which two animals travel the same speed?_____

Facts taken from Guinness Book of World Records, 1989 Edition

☞ Pay attention to the signs. Check any 10 problems.

39.6 - 4.57 =

27 + 6.438 =

307.87 - 298.923 =

48.609 - 22.306 =

77.3 + 16.882 =

92 - 6.27 =

3780.5 + 298.5 + .5 =

$40.26 - 35.87 =

84.93 + 26.109 =

90 - .629 =

200 - 2.46 =

678.39 - 287 =

92.06 + 13.145 =

307.28 - .928 =

42.37 - 5.4 =

84 - 38.541 =

In the U.S., Connecticut has the highest income per person. People in Conn. earn 130.5% above the national average. New Jersey is second with 121.6% and New York is third with 109%.

1. What is the difference in income between the average person living in Conn. and N. J.?_____

2. Between a person living in N. J. and N. Y.?_____

3. Between a person living in Conn. and N. Y.?_____

Over a nine year period (1927-35), Garapan, Saipan, (Mariana Islands, Pacific Ocean) had the most level temperatures. The lowest temperature was 67.3°F and the highest temperature was 88.5°F. The highest temperature ever recorded in the *shade* (136.4°F) was in Libya.

4. The most the temperature ever varied in Garapan was _____.

5. What was the difference between Garapan's highest temp. and Libya's?_____

The fastest track motorcycles are geared to run at least 186.4 mph. The record snowmobile speed is 158.53 mph. The speed record for bicycles is 61.94 mph. The highest speed for a rocket-powered ice sled was 247.93 mph. The *Steamin" Demon* set the steam car record of 145.607 mph.

6. How much faster would a motorcycle be than the *Steamin' Demon* ?_____

7. How much slower was the snowmobile than the motorcycle?_____

8. Snowmobiles can go how much faster than a bicycle?_____

9. The rocket-powered ice sled ran how much faster than the snowmobile?_____

10. The *Steamin' Demon* was how much slower than the ice sled?_____

11. The fastest bicycle was still_____ slower than the rocket-powered sled.

All records taken from Guiness Book of World Records, 1989 edition.

You should feel very confident about addition and subtraction with decimal numbers by now. Addition and subtraction, because they are opposites, use the same rule essentially - line up the decimal point and _____.
  Multiplication, however, uses a different rule. The multiplication rule says:

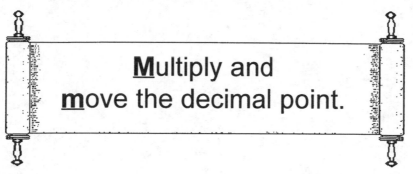

Multiply and
move the decimal point.

  Multiplication of decimals is no harder than regular multiplication. The only difference is putting the decimal point in your answer. Since the decimal can't be put into an answer until you have an answer, you multiply first and place the decimal point last. Multiplication is as easy as M & M - **m**ultiply and **m**ove.
  Let's look at some examples of multiplying decimals.

$423 .14	423 .14 ②	2 .312 ③	4.31 ③
x ___2	x ___2	x ___1	x __.2
$846.28	846.28	2.312	.0862

  The first two problems are the same except for the dollar sign. In the money problem, how many decimal places did you have?_____ How many decimal places do you have in your answer?_____ In the second problem, how many decimal places do you have?_____ How many decimal places does your answer have?_____
  In your third and fourth examples, you also have digits filling decimal places. The **total number of decimal places in the problem must equal the total number of decimal places in your answer.**

Before you can move the decimal point, you must know how many places to move it. An easy way to count the TOTAL number of decimal places in a problem is to draw a line through the decimal points. Then count the digits on the decimal side of the line. The first problem is done for you.
☞ Do **not** try to solve these problems. Draw a line through the decimal points, connecting them. Count the **TOTAL** number of decimal places (digits to the right of the line) in each problem. Write the **TOTAL** number of decimal places on the decimal side of your problem and circle it. Again, **DO NOT TRY TO SOLVE THESE PROBLEMS.**

2.93 ③	.4376	245.2	3.0894
x __.4	x __.345	x __.06	x 94.07

94.992	16.0043	7.772	.0236
x 5.367	x .30498	x 24.3	x __12

Now you know how to count the decimal places in each problem, you'll know how far to move the decimal point. Let's look at some examples.

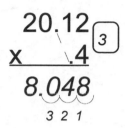

20.12
x   .4
8.048
3 2 1

Multiply the problem.
How many decimal places are there in the entire problem?_____
Since you are only interested in decimal places, start on the decimal side of your answer (the right end) and count backwards _____ places. Write your decimal point at that spot!

☞ These problems have been solved for you. Without a decimal point, however, they are wrong answers. Count the decimal places in the problem. Then place the decimal point in its correct place.

9.34	16.7	5.554	906.13
x 2.4	x .98	x .447	x 3.426
22416	16366	2482638	31044013

24.037	17.52	.9986	2.394
x .18	x .9	x 2.4	x 15
432666	15768	239664	35910

52.367 x 4.189 = 21936536   204 x .329 = 67116

3.25 x .6783 = 2204475   .87305 x 2.9 = 2531845

81.4 x 62.3 = 507122   857.03 x 12.7 = 10884281

Reproduction restricted.

What happens in a problem where you don't have enough numbers and still need to move the decimal point farther? Remember **ZERO PLACE HOLDERS**? In the past, you put your zero place holders on the **end** of the decimal - this didn't change the number's worth at all.

But now the number doesn't have enough digits and **needs its worth changed**. Putting zero place holders on the end of the decimal won't do you any good. This number doesn't have enough digits because **it isn't small** enough. You must make it smaller by **adding zeros in front of the number**.

Let's <u>look at</u> and <u>think about</u> the example:

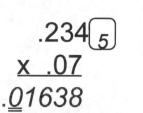

> You are multiplying two very small numbers. Neither number is even worth 1. Therefore, your answer is going to be a very small number, probably less than 1 also.
>
> In this example, you will need to move your decimal _____ places. The problem is that you only have 4 places to move the decimal point - and you <u>need more places</u>.
>
> Adding a zero onto the end of the digits wouldn't change its value. Putting a **zero in front** of the digits would make the number small enough. Now there are enough places.

Changing the answer to make it smaller is only necessary in multiplication and division. When you are multiplying by two very small numbers, both of which are less than one, this will happen often. Just remember to change the value to **make it smaller <u>whenever necessary</u>**.

☞ All of these problems have been solved for you. You must place the decimal point. Count the decimal places and put your decimal point in the correct spot.

.296	3.24	.6789	34.7
x .32	x .04	x 1.12	x .007
9472	1296	760368	2429

56.71	.152	1.0036	.5
x .004	x .63	x .007	x .1
22684	9576	70252	5

2.18	.902	.6341	5.25
x .002	x .4	x .05	x .012
436	3608	31705	63

Before you actually begin multiplication, you need to think a moment about what you have learned. Ignoring zero as a possible number, let's review. Think about what happens in the problem when you:

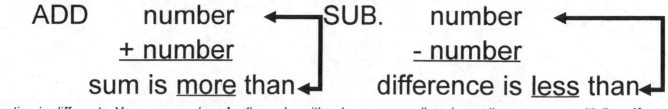

ADD   number   ←┐ SUB.   number   ←┐
          + number   - number
          sum is <u>more</u> than ←┘   difference is <u>less</u> than ←┘

Multiplication is different. Your answer (**product**) can be either larger or smaller, depending on your multiplier. If you have multiplied by a number larger than one, your answer will be **more** than your starting number. If you multiply by a number less than one, your answer will be **less** than your starting number. Let's look at two examples using the same numerals, but putting the decimal point in a different place in your multiplier.

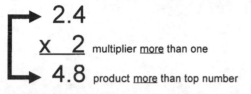

┌→ 2.4
│ x 2 multiplier <u>more</u> than one
└→ 4.8 product <u>more</u> than top number

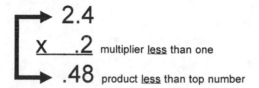

┌→ 2.4
│ x .2 multiplier <u>less</u> than one
└→ .48 product <u>less</u> than top number

Thinking about your **products** (answers) before you multiply helps you to double check your answer. Problems multiplied by numbers **more than one** will give you answers which are **more** than your top number. Problems multiplied by numbers **less then one** will give products which are **less** than your top number.

Think about your product before you start. Ask yourself if it will be more or less than your top number. This will give you an idea of how large your answer should be. Then you can double check after you've placed your decimal point.

Now you are ready to **M & M = Multiply and move!** It's as easy as 1, 2, 3.

(1) **Multiply** the problem regularly, as if there were no decimals in it.
(2) **Count** the total decimal places in the problem.
(3) **Move** your decimal point into the correct place in your product (answer).

| 2.3 | 64.1 | 1.97 | .54 |
| x 4 | x .5 | x .3 | x 2 |

| .508 | 7.06 | 30.4 | 9.0053 |
| x 6 | x .3 | x 8 | x .5 |

| 26.47 | 13.058 | .6032 | 11.9 |
| x .4 | x 7 | x .9 | x .5 |

☞   Find your products in these harder problems. **M & M!**

24.52 x .4	30.94 x .53	2.93 x 62	4.3 x .9
43.76 x 8.1	61.05 x .07	8.203 x .36	.965 x 8
49.05 x .19	7.204 x 4.5	.0238 x .56	18 x .3
3.94 x .03	71.62 x .98	5.031 x 4.4	.684 x 5
42.03 x 2.4	51.73 x .7	806 x 6.2	9.601 x 8.3

1. Space shuttle crews need special suits when they go outside the shuttle. Since 1982, these EVA (extra-vehicular activity) suits have cost $2.3 million dollars each. An average crew is 5 people. How much would a crew's suits cost?_____

2. In Jan. 1985, the most expensive food in the world cost $60 per .44 oz. How much would 7 cans of these truffles cost?_____ How many ounces would you get for your money?_____

3. The longest salami on record was 58.75 ft. long and weighed 863.5 lbs. If someone made one twice as long, how long would it be?_____ It would weigh_____.

4. The longest banana split ever made was 4.39 miles long. How long would the split be if someone made it one and a half times as long?_____

5. The largest single serving of instant mashed potatoes was mixed in a concrete truck. The potatoes weighed 18,260 lbs. How much would a half dozen loads weigh?____

6. Some people like to push baby carriages. In 24 hrs. time, 57 California runners pushed a carriage 345.25 mi. In England, a 10 man team pushed a carriage with an adult "baby" 252.65 mi. How much farther did the California team push their carriage?_____ If the California team could push their empty carriage at record pace for 3 days, how far would they go?_____ The English team, at record pace, might go how far in 5 days?_____

Did you notice how long your answers were getting? Some were five or more decimal places. When decimal numbers get that long, they cause a lot of trouble. **Rounding off to significant digits** makes them easier to manage. Rounding lets you work with only two (hundredths) or three (thousandths) decimal places and forget the other itty bitty ones.

Decimals round **one place only**. The directions tell you which place to check. This place only changes when the <u>smaller next door neighbor</u> is worthwhile, **5 (half) or more**. Let's look at the following example:

round .06392 to the nearest <u>hundredth</u>

Ask yourself: Which place does the directions want me to check?_____ What digit is there?_____

Now look at the **smaller** decimal place right next door (thousandths). What digit is in the thousandths place?_____ This **next door** digit determines whether the hundredths place must change. Is the **next door digit half or more** (5 or above)? If the answer is "**yes**", then the hundredths place goes **up** in value to a seven. If the answer is "**no**", the next door digit isn't worth much and the hundredths place **remains the same**. In our example, the **next door digit** is 3. Three is <u>not</u> more than five, so we leave .06 alone and drop the extra places (the 3, 9, and 2). The <u>rounded</u> answer is .06.

Let's look at another example:

round 3.456801 to the nearest <u>thousandth</u>

What digit is in the thousandths place?_____ What digit is the smaller next door neighbor?_____ Is it 5 or higher?_____ Then you need to **round the thousandths place up, increasing** the 6 to a 7. Everything else stays the same. Drop all numerals after the thousandths place (the 8, 0, and 1). Your <u>rounded</u> answer is 3.45<u>7</u>.

To round off, then, you must:

(1) find the place the directions ask you to check

(2) check the next door neighbor - if 5 or higher, round up; if less than 5, leave it alone

(3) drop extra digits, beginning with the next door digit (you don't need him anymore).

Rounding is used when you don't need to be exact. *You only round on tests when you are told to do so.*

═══

☞   Round these numbers to the nearest **hundredth**.

(1) 23.4681 =

(2) 47.07369 =

(3) 400.00931 =

(4) 5.8719 =

(5) 2871.6235 =

(6) 9.287103 =

(7) .55544 =

(8) 324.08614 =

(9) 4.328007 =

(10) 15.2555 =

(11) 901.0042 =

(12) 200.11319 =

When working money problems, you always round off to the **nearest cent** (unless the directions specifically tell you to do otherwise). When you round off to the nearest cent, you are really <u>rounding to the hundredths place</u>.

Here is an example:

Place the decimal point into your answer _____ places back. What digit is in the hundreds (cents) place?_____ What digit is in its smaller neighbor?_____ Therefore, you round off the 2, making it a _____, and drop the smaller neighbor ___. Put in your dollar sign and you are finished.

It's not hard. Just remember to **always** round off to the nearest <u>cent</u>.

☞ Round these problems to the **nearest cent**.

$23.58
x   .3

$8.95
x   .5

$34.89
x   6

$70.05
x   .4

$15.63
x   .04

$90.40
x   .07

$218.03
x   .08

$29.59
x   .09

$60.78
x   .25

$42.00
x   .75

$18.95
x   3.5

$50.29
x   4.6

$48.16
x   .6

$56.09
x 3.19

$75.00
x   .68

$62.75
x 45.2

☞   Round to the nearest **hundredth**.

43.7	.24	5.081	96
x .6	x .73	x 3.45	x 8.2

$83.06	246	10.15	$29.45
x 3.47	x .8	x 6.4	x 250

63.8 x 14.2 =   392 x .5 =

4.519 x .75 = $5.13 x 35.8 =

7.0832 x 25 = $14.75 x 6.41 =

3098 x .206 =   678.9 x 1.23 =

☞ Round these numbers to the nearest **hundredth**. Be careful and watch your signs.

2.943 x 16.5 =   467.3 + 8.921 =

57.603 - 14.7149 =   50.92 x .6 =

93.041 - 6.0095 =   6.34 x 1.9 =

7.0328 + .046 + .93 =   80.705 - .9395 =

17.23 x .25 =   428.002 + 6.0089 =

8 - 3.592 =   500 x 2.87 =

73.645 + 17.4 + .867 =   410.9 x 5 =

☞   Round the following answers to the nearest **tenth** or **cent**.

$7.04 x 1.4 =   32.006 - 14.0872 =

58.92 x .61 =   75.3 + 2.9065 =

69.093 - .0732 =   46.23 x .428 =

.246 x 3.45 =   63 + .4986 =

750 - 1.6239 =   248.754 + .99 =

$30.81 x .6 =   40 - .2755 =

530 x .157 =   6.28 + 3.945 + .0089 =

In Biblical times, people used different weights and measures than we use today. They did not use decimals either. To get a feel for their weights and measurements, solve these **difficult** word problems using the charts below.

Prices as of Jan. 24, 1990	
Silver	
N.Y.	$5.275/oz.
Gold	
London	$413.25/oz.
Frankfurt	$409.55/oz.
N.Y.	$408.25/oz.

Biblical times	Value today
Minah	20 oz.
Shekel	.4 oz.
Talent	75.5 lbs.

1. The queen of Sheba gave King Solomon 120 talents of gold. How many lbs. of gold did she give him?_____ I KINGS 10:10

2. King Solomon made 200 shields of gold. Six hundred shekels of gold went into each shield. How many ounces were in 1 shield?_____ How much would <u>one</u> shield cost if the gold was bought in London?_____ N.Y.?_____

3. The gold that Solomon collected in one year was 666 talents. How many lbs. of gold did this equal?_____

4. In the days of Solomon, silver was not important (I KINGS 10:21). Today, how much would 5 shekels of silver cost?_____

5. How much would a minah of gold from London cost?_____ From Frankfurt?_____ From N.Y.?_____

6. How much would a minah of silver cost today?_____

7. A talent equals 60 minahs. 60 minahs = _____ oz. A talent of gold from Frankfurt would cost?_____

8. Which of the three cities has the cheapest gold price?_____   Gold prices from Asheville Citizen-Times, Jan. 24, 1990, pg. 6B

You see percentages all the time.

Big Sale - 25% off   10% tithe   prices slashed - 50%
You made an 88 on your test   14% FINANCING
5% state sales tax   rain - 70% chance   6% interest on checking

These are all examples of percentages. To solve a percentage problem. you need know what the percent means. Percents are based on **100**. An easy way to remember this is that the word "per**cents**" has the smaller word "**cents**" in it. There are **100 cents** in a dollar. One hundred percent (**100%**) of anything = the **whole thing**.

100% = the wole thing

Now, let's look at some of the above examples to understand percentages better.

Big Sale - 25% off =

$ .25 saved	$ .75 out of every dollar still must paid

The regular, normal price is 100%. Stores emphasize what you don't pay (the $.25 discount), rather than what you must pay ($.75) (25¢+75¢=$1). This sounds better to the customer than telling them they still owe 75% to buy the item.

10% tithe =

$ .10	$ .90 is yours to spend or save

God allows you to earn money with work he has provided and strength to do it. People thank God by repaying Him 10% of this money (tithe). That means, for every 100 cents earned, God gets $.10 and you keep $.90 (10¢+90¢=$1.00).

prices slashed 50% =

$ .50 is saved	$ .50 is paid

At the regular price, you would have had to pay all 100 cents for each dollar of the cost (100%). Now the regular price has been reduced and you only need to pay half. You save $.50 and pay $.50 (50¢+50¢=$1.00).

You made an 88 on your test =

you got 88% of the problems correct	12%

To be able to compare test results easily, all tests are worth 100 possible points. Depending on the number of questions, each problem will be worth a certain amount of these 100 possible points. If you get all of the questions correct, you score 100%. However, in the example above, you didn't get all of them right. If the test contained 100 questions, this 88% would mean that you missed 12 of them (each problem was worth 1 point each). On a short test of 8 problems, missing only one problem would give you an 88% (each problem was worth 12 points).   The fewer the problems, the more each problem is worth. Missing 2 out of a 4 problem test would be half (50%) wrong!

14% FINANCING =

pay back 100% of the money you borrowed	+ 14%

To use someone else's money, you must pay a user's fee. In this case, you must pay all of the money back *plus* an additional 14¢ for each and every dollar you borrowed - that's $14.00 extra on a $100, $140.00 on a $1000, $1,400 on $10,000, etc. This really adds up when you must pay this additional charge *every year* for *several years!*

5% state sales tax =

$1.00	+ 5%

Most states have a sales tax, usually between 4 and 10%. This money is used for many different things (paying policemen, repairing roads, etc.). In this case, you must pay an extra nickel to the state for each dollar you spend .

rain - 70% chance =

70% chance that it will rain	30% it won't

Weather conditions have been recorded for a long time. When weather conditions were like this, it rained an average of 70 out of 100 times. Anything over 50% (half) supposedly has a good chance of happening.

6% interest on checking =

$1.00 of your money in the bank	+ 6%

Most banks pay you additional money to leave your money with them. In this case, you earn 6¢ for each dollar you have in your checking account (or one half cent every month). Every little bit helps. You make money by not spending it.

Percentages are not hard. They can be discounts or additional payments. Either way, they are written as a decimal, **just like cents**. If you remember PER**CENTS**, and write your decimal like money without a dollar sign, you'll never be wrong. And, as you will see, working with them will be nothing more than **multiplication of decimals in disguise**.

Do the problems on the next page.

☞   Write these amounts in decimal format. Start with the whole number and move the understood decimal **2 spaces to the left**. Use zero place holders when necessary.

example: 5¢ = **$.05**

(1) 35¢ =_____   (2) 7¢ =_____

(3) 4¢ =_____   (4) 75¢ =_____

(5) 19¢ =_____   (6) 1¢ =_____

To work with percents, you must learn to change percents to decimals and back again. Each change requires you to move your decimal point **2 places** in a certain direction. There is an easy way to remember which way to move the decimal point.

Remember your alphabet? (A B C **D** E F G H I J K L M N O **P** Q R S T U V W X Y Z) The "d" in **d**ecimal is to the left of the "p" in **p**ercent. Along the alphabet, to move from "**p**" to "**d**", you would move to the left. So, whenever you **change from percents to decimals, move the decimal point 2 places to the left**. Move your "understood" decimal point.

example: 14% = **.14**

(7) 29% =_____   (8) 3% =_____

(9) 50% =_____   (10) 64% =_____

(11) 9% =_____   (12) 7% =_____

(13) 5% =_____   (14) 33% =_____

(15) 38% =_____   (16) 1% =_____

☞   You moved the "understood" decimal point **2 spaces to the left** to change a percent to a decimal. In percentages that already contain a decimal point, follow the same rule: move that existing decimal point over **2 more spaces to the left**. You always move **2 spaces**. Write these numbers as decimals.

example: 12.5% = **.125** (read as 12 and a half percent)

(17) 9.25% =_____   (18) 14.5% =_____

(19) .25% =_____   (20) 6.75% =_____

(21) 2.35% =_____   (22) 18.33% =_____

(23) 4% =_____   (24) 36% =_____

(25) 92.3% =_____   (26) 81.6% =_____

(27) .5% =_____   (28) 7.75% =_____

(29) .893% =_____   (30) 5.5% =_____

(31) 4.9% =_____   (32) 18.35% =_____

(33) 2.33% =_____   (34) 99.994% =_____

(35) .75% =_____   (36) 100% =_____

☞   Write the numbers as words. Don't forget to use half, third, quarter, etc.
    example: .75% = **three quarters of one percent**   2.5% = **two and a half percent**

(1) 19.5% =_____

(2) 4.25% =_____

(3) 8.33% =_____

(4) .5% =_____

(5) 1.75% =_____

☞   Consider these discounts. What do they mean **in words**.
    example: 33% off = **one third off = pay only 67ø for each dollar's worth of goods**

(6) 25% off = _____ off = pay _____ instead of a dollar

(7) 50% off =_____ off = pay _____ instead of a dollar

(8) 75% off =_____ off = pay _____ instead of a dollar

(9) 66% off =_____ off = pay _____ instead of a dollar

(10) 10% off =_____ off = pay _____ instead of a dollar

☞   Find these percentages from your local area.

(11) your state sales tax =_____

(12) your state gasoline tax (if any)=_____

(13) interest paid at your bank on a savings account=_____

(14) interest on U.S. Savings bonds =_____

(15) best sale on clothes in today's paper =____, store _____

(16) your highest grade this week = ____, subject_____

Now you are ready to find out how much those percentages equal. Percentages are relative. That means a percentage may be good in one situation, but not so good in another. An 8% store discount isn't much. Getting 8% interest on a savings account that the <u>bank pays to you</u> is quite good. A 25% store discount, on the other hand, is pretty good. **Paying 25%** interest on a loan to a bank is very high and almost unreasonable. Sometimes the percentage is in your favor and sometimes it isn't.

To work a problem involving a percent:

(1) change the percent to a decimal number
(2) M & M (multiply and move)

That's all there is to it. Here are some examples:

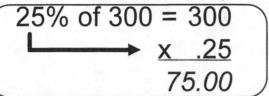

$$25\% \text{ of } 300 = 300$$
$$\times \ .25$$
$$75.00$$

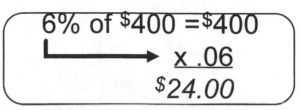

$$6\% \text{ of } ^\$400 = ^\$400$$
$$\times .06$$
$$^\$24.00$$

In the first problem, you can drop the two zero place holders. It is like rounding them off - they just aren't necessary. However, in the second sample problem, the two zero place holders should stay. Why? Because you are talking about money and it is good to leave the cents there (even when there aren't any).

☞ Solve these problems. Round off to **nearest hundredth,** leaving the cents.

(1) 15% of 200 =   (2) 20% of 900 =

(3) 50% of $652 =   (4) 25% of 786 =

(5) 75% of 240 =   (6) 33% of 750 =

(7) .5% of 300 =   (8) 2.5% of 500 =

(9) 30% of 560 =   (10) 100% of 200 =

(11) 65% of 300 =   (12) 90% of 300 =

There is a **shortcut** in multiplication. It is used <u>only</u> when there are zeros at the end of your whole numbers. Look at these examples:

200
x .10

Count the zeros at the end of your numbers. How many do you see?_____
These were <u>at the end</u> of your numbers and will <u>stay at the end</u> of your product.
Multiply 1x2 =_____ (Your answer **so far** is 2 with 3 zeros = 2000)
Move in your decimal point = _____
Round off any unnecessary zeros. Your answer is_____.

Here's another one.

3000
x .25

Count the zeros. How many do you see?_____
Multiply 3x25 =_____ (Your answer **so far** is _____)
Move in your decimal point = _____
Round off any unnecessary zeros. Your answer is_____.

Any easier than multiplying everything? This **shortcut** really comes in handy when you have lots of zeros.

☞   Solve these problems using the shortcut method described above.

(1) 55% of 4000 =

(2) 20% of 1500 =

(3) 18% of 900 =

(4) 70% of 20,000 =

(5) 30% of 585 =

(6) 66% of 10,000 =

(7) 4% of 6,000 =

(8) 50% of 80 =

(9) 20% of 5,000 =

(10) 45% of 9,000 =

(11) 70% of 6,500 =

(12) 80% of 40,000 =

       Reproduction restricted.

Percentage problems often can be figured in several ways. This is because percentage problems usually want you to find more than one answer. Problems can be broken down into steps.

We will use ***tithing*** as an example. No one knows when the practice of tithing began, but it is commanded by God ("Bring the whole tithe into the storehouse, that there may be food in my house. Test me in this," says the Lord Almighty, "and see if I will not throw open the floodgates of heaven and pour out so much blessing that you will not have room enough for it." Malachi 3:10 NIV).

Abram made the first recorded 10% tithe to Melchizedek (Genesis 14:17-24). Because Melchizedek was both king and priest, Abram gave him this gift as a holy gift to God. This 10% tithe meant that God got 10% of everything Abram had (animals, crops, money, etc). Abram kept the remaining 90% with which God had so generously blessed him.

Let's use the same example and figure it two ways. If you like to multiply better than subtract, often you can work it out making 2 multiplication problems. Just remember to have both percentages equal 100% (10% + 90% = 100%).

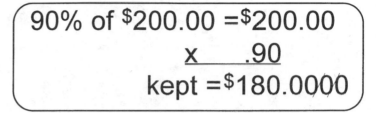

```
10% of $200.00 = $200.00           90% of $200.00 = $200.00
                x    .10                           x    .90
   tithe paid = $20.0000              kept = $180.0000
```

If you like to multiply and subtract, then you can work problems using both processes.

```
10% of $200.00 = $200.00           the amount = $200.00
                x    .10            tithe paid = - 20.00
                  $20.0000                kept = $180.00
```

☞ People feel led by God to tithe different amounts. The minimum tithe is 10%. There is no maximum. Read about the people below. Use the **zero shortcut** with either method.

Name	tithe (%)	earnings	tithe paid	money kept
Jim	10%	$225.00	_____	_____
Mary	12%	$135.00	_____	_____
Fred	14%	$115.50	_____	_____
Lauren	10%	$89.00	_____	_____
Your Dad	_____	_____	_____	_____
You	_____	_____	_____	_____

Every year, the economy changes. Prices go up on almost everything. In order for people to be able to afford to continue buying things (goods), their pay also needs to increase. Many work places have a built in **cost of living pay increase**. This is usually a percentage of a worker's **annual** (or yearly) salary, somewhere around 5%. Five cents on a dollar doesn't sound like much of an increase, but every little bit helps when raising a family.

To find a worker's cost of living raise, multiply his annual salary by the percent of increase (usually 5%). Because it is a pay **increase**, you will **add** this amount to the first annual salary. This new total is the worker's <u>new</u> annual salary.

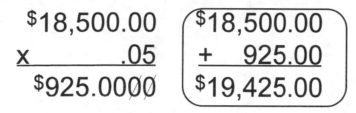

Sometimes, companies must **cut wages** to stay in business. Most times, employees feel it is better to keep a job, even at lower wages, than to lose the job and **all** wages while they hunt for another job. Had it been a **cut** in wages, you would have **decreased** or **subtracted** the amount. This is how a decrease would be solved.

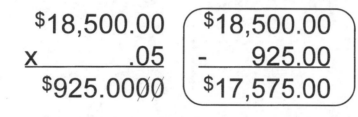

Does your father get an **annual cost of living increase**?_____ It is a nice way to get a yearly raise.

☞ Round to the **nearest cent**.

1) Sam's business is great. He is giving all of his workers a 5% raise. Jack earns $18,457.00 a year. How much will his pay increase?_____ What is his new salary?_____

2) Larry is losing business. He must take a 5% salary cut to have more money for the business. He earned $14,895.00 this year. How much less will he earn next year?_____ What will his new salary be?_____

3) Jerry got a 5% raise on his $17,535.00 salary? How much more will he earn?_____ His new salary is _____.

4) Marge's business lost 8% from last year's earnings ($47,302.00). Loss = _____ Earnings = _____

You may use **complementary numbers** to find percentages. Something that **complements** another thing, **completes** it. In this case, our complementary numbers <u>must equal 100</u> to be a complete whole (100%). So, when we **add two numbers together**, they must **equal 100**. If you have a 25% discount, you will pay 75% of the price (25+75=100). If you pay a 10% tithe, you keep 90% of the money (10+90=100). If you pay 65% of the price, you are getting a 35% discount (65+35=100).

Let's say you are in a store having a 25% discount sale. You probably don't care how much you are saving. You just want to know how much the item will cost you. Use the example of $40.00 worth of clothing. Twenty-five percent of the amount is what you save; 75% of the amount is what you pay (25%+75%=100% or the whole price). The example will solve for both savings and payment. Solve for the answer needed.

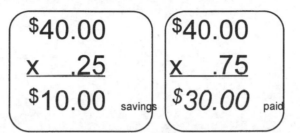

$$
\begin{array}{r} \$40.00 \\ \text{x} \quad .25 \\ \hline \$10.00 \end{array} \text{ savings}
\qquad
\begin{array}{r} \$40.00 \\ \text{x} \quad .75 \\ \hline \$30.00 \end{array} \text{ paid}
$$

This is a very handy way to figure percentages and can be used **in any situation**. When in doubt, use this method.

☞   Round to the nearest <u>cent</u>.

1) Leslie is buying a $25.95 gift for her parent's anniversary. The store has the gift at 35% off. She will pay?_____

2) Marty saved $95.80. He wants to tithe 12%. How much will he pay his church?_____

3) Jo runs a bookstore. Their records are 25% off. How much does a $9.95 album cost during this sale?_____

4) Maxine earned $14.75 babysitting. She wants to put 15% in the bank. How much should she deposit?_____

5) Manuel pays 12% of his earnings to his parents for room and board. Last week, he earned $85. How much will he have left?_____ How much will he pay?_____

6) Lorraine made an 86 on her test paper. There were 36 problems on the page. How many did she miss?_____

7) Jan's 6% pay cut on $275/wk. means _____ less money.

☞   Round off your answers to the nearest penny or the hundredths place.

1) Max has $358.42 in his savings account. His bank pays 5.25% annual interest. He should earn _____ in interest.

2) Hannah made a 94% on her 50 problem test. How many did she get right?_____   Wrong?_____

3) Q-mart is having a 33% off sale on men's $6.95 packages of socks. How much will Ben save on **2** packs?_____

4) Today's weather forecast says there is 30% chance of rain. How much chance of good weather is there? _____ Do you think it will rain with a 30% chance?_____

5) Marvin earned $12.75 mowing the neighbor's yard, $4.85 babysitting, and $3.75 for around-the-house chores. How much did he earn this week?_____   He wants to save 15%. How much should he set aside for savings?_____

6). Computer Outlet has a 20% off sale. The software Sam needs costs $39.95. What will it cost on sale?_____

7) Foster earned $24,372.64 last year. He had to pay 12.5% in income taxes. How much tax did he pay?_____

8) Ethan borrowed $2,000 for one year. His finance rate was 14%. How much additional must he pay in finance charges, over and above the loan?_____

9) Stacey had 246 items to sell at a flea market. She sold half. How many did she sell?_____   Bring home?_____

10) On a 28 problem test, a score of 75 means _____ right.

In figuring **state sales tax**, first you must know if your state charges sales tax on the item you are buying and the rate, or percentage, they charge. Like other percentages, sales tax can be figured more than one way. The way you choose is determined by the information the question needs.

Do you need to know exactly how much tax is charged?

Jack bought a bike for $69.99. He must pay 5% sales tax. How much is the sales tax he must pay?_____

If the question asks you how much sales tax was paid, you must work the problem this way.

$$5\% \text{ of } \$69.99 = \begin{array}{r} \$69.99 \\ \times \quad .05 \\ \hline \$3.4995 \end{array}$$ round off $3.4995 to _____

In real life, there is one **exception** to the **rounding off rule**. Stores <u>never</u> lose money on the rounded penny. The **customer must always pay** it to the store. Those pennies could add up to thousands of dollars in a busy store. Each customer doesn't miss an extra penny here or there. On tests, however, ROUND CORRECTLY.

The question did not ask you how much Jack paid for the bike. If it had, you would have had one more step - adding the tax amount to the price of the bike. This would have given you the total price paid for the bike.

$$\begin{array}{r} \$69.99 \\ + \quad 3.50 \\ \hline \$73.49 \end{array}$$

1) Mark is buying deodorant for $2.49, a shirt for $11.99, and socks for $4.29. How much is his purchase?_____
He must pay 6% sales tax. How much is the tax?_____
Mark must pay a total of _____.

2) Sadie chose $29.45 worth of groceries. Her state charges 5.5% sales tax. She will pay for the sales tax?_____

3) Jeff bought a record for $9.98, a book for $7.95, and a gift for $8.39. With 6% sales tax, what is his total?_____

4) Katie bought a $10.98 stuffed animal for her baby sister. Sales tax is 6.5%. How much tax does she owe?_____

5) Jan paid 4.5% sales tax on a $14.58 purchase. What was his final total?_____   How much sales tax?_____

Reproduction restricted.

There is a **shortcut** for **finding totals** when you <u>don't need to know</u> each different amount. Let's look at an example.
Kyle paid 6.5% sales tax on his new $56.95 pup tent. What was his total bill?_____
In this example, you are only asked to **find the total**. None of the individual parts, like sales tax, need to be shown.
You could work this problem like those on the previous page. FOR THIS BOOK, remember that the store gets the penny.

6.5% of $56.95 = $56.95   round off to $3.71
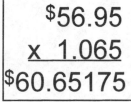   add to   + $56.95
$3.70175   total $60.66

Or you could solve the whole problem in one step. One times your amount will give you your starting amount, right?
When working with percentages, 1 whole equals 100%, right? When you multiply the percentage, find the total price by
adding a 100% to your percentage. This will make your multiplier **1. (percentage)**

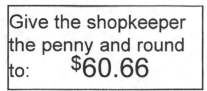

The **shortcut** may look more confusing than it really is. All it amounts to is adding one whole to your percentage and
multiply. This **shortcut** can be used any time you must pay the whole price plus a percentage for a **final total**. It can be
used in finance charges (you pay the bank the whole loan <u>plus</u> an extra percentage), sales taxes, etc.

1) Sue bought a $15,640 car. She had to pay 3% sales tax.
How much did the car cost her?_____

2) Ashe financed a $4,500 balloon loan at 11.5%. He must
pay how much to pay the loan off?_____

3) Margaret bought a new muffler for $89.95. Sales tax was
7.5%. How much did she pay in tax?_____ Total?_____

4) Janice paid 4.33% tax on a $28.75 purchase. How much
was her final bill?_____

5) Wayne must pave a 2,450 ft. section of road. He is 65%
finished. How many feet has he paved?_____ How
much does he have to go?_____

6) Matt paid_____ for a $129.95 purchase with 5.25%
sales tax.

☞ Get your local newspaper. Find the sale advertisements. Write 10 word problems and solve them.

PERFECTING THE POINT   DIVISION

Now you are ready to begin **division**. Again, division is easy when you remember that it is the opposite of multiplication. You moved the decimal point in multiplication; you also will move the decimal point in division. The rule for division is:

Move the decimal point and _divide._

In multiplication, you multiplied first and moved the decimal point last. In division, you **move the decimal point first**, and then divide last. The reason for this is not show up on these first few pages. It will be explained to you on a later page. For right now, you will move the decimal point **straight up** into your answer (**quotient**) and **divide**. That way you won't forget to place it in your answer. Just don't forget it!

You moved your decimal point before in money. You move it the same way now - **straight up** into your quotient (answer).

$$\begin{array}{r} \$2.34 \\ 2\overline{)\$4.68} \end{array} \qquad \begin{array}{r} 2.3 \\ 2\overline{)4.6} \end{array} \qquad \begin{array}{r} .23 \\ 3\overline{).69} \end{array} \qquad \begin{array}{r} 20.1202 \\ 4\overline{)80.4808} \end{array}$$

☞ Solve the following problems. Don't forget to move your decimal **straight up into your dividend.** You may use long or short division.

$$3\overline{)6.93} \qquad 4\overline{).8048} \qquad 2\overline{)6.482} \qquad 3\overline{)9.0936}$$

$$5\overline{).5205} \qquad 6\overline{).672} \qquad 7\overline{)1.428} \qquad 8\overline{)640.816}$$

DIVISION

PERFECTING THE POINT

☞ Use long division to solve these problems.

$$8\overline{)6.424}$$

$$5\overline{)62.030}$$

$$2\overline{)97.274}$$

$$4\overline{)270.8}$$

$$9\overline{)2.0736}$$

$$3\overline{).0057}$$

$$3\overline{)14.58}$$

$$6\overline{)19.44}$$

$$2\overline{)7.036}$$

$$7\overline{)\$85.40}$$

$$5\overline{)\$498.35}$$

$$4\overline{)2.272}$$

PERFECTING THE POINT

In division, you have two numbers - one outside the division sign (the **divisor**) and one under the division sign (the **dividend**). You divide these and get an answer (the **quotient**). In words, the problem looks like this:

$$\text{divisor } \overline{)\text{dividend}}^{\text{quotient}}$$

So far, you have divided a decimal number by a whole divisor. What happens when your divisor is a **decimal number**? For one thing, your quotient will be bigger than your dividend. But you must add one step to your division rule **before** you divide - **move both decimal points**.

Decimal number divisors **must** be changed to a **whole number** before you can divide. To do that, **move the decimal point** on your divisor **to the right**, making it a whole number. Remember how many places you moved the divisor's decimal point. Now move the dividend's decimal point to the **right** the **same number of places**. Without moving the decimal point equally in **both** divisor and dividend, your quotient will be wrong.

$$2.\overline{)4.6} \quad \text{becomes} \quad 2.\overline{)46.}^{23.}$$

Remember the old cliche, "What's good enough for the goose is good enough for the gander?" Well, think of the **divisor** as the goose and the **dividend** as the gander. You can't change one's worth without changing the other's. **Both** need the **same decimal point movement**. **Move the decimal point to the right the same number of spaces.** If you don't **move the decimal point for both,** you will lay a bad egg for an answer!

☞ Move the decimal point to make decimal numbers into whole numbers.

$$.6\overline{)3.690} \qquad .3\overline{)124.5} \qquad .5\overline{)4685} \qquad .7\overline{)43.54}$$

$$4.\overline{)8.268} \qquad 2\overline{)75.4} \qquad .8\overline{).184} \qquad .9\overline{)18.81}$$

PERFECTING THE POINT   DIVISION

☞ Be careful. Move the decimal point only when necessary.

$.3 \overline{)\,.465}$

$4 \overline{)\,\$25.00}$

$.7 \overline{)\,639.1}$

$8 \overline{)\,57.608}$

$5 \overline{)\,.0275}$

$.6 \overline{)\,3.4806}$

$.2 \overline{)\,7.054}$

$3 \overline{)\,52.848}$

$.9 \overline{)\,55.08}$

$.5 \overline{)\,.0490}$

$.4 \overline{)\,5.92}$

$7 \overline{)\,\$268.31}$

PERFECTING THE POINT

DIVISION

So far, so good. But what happens when you must move the decimal point in the divisor and have run out of numbers in the dividend? **ZERO PLACE HOLDERS!** You can **add as many as you need**! They don't change the value of your **final quotient**

$$240.$$
$$.2 \overline{)48} \quad \text{becomes} \quad 2.\overline{)480}$$

When you moved your decimal points **one place to the right**, you multiplied both your divisor and your dividend by 10 (.2×10=2 and 48×10=480). You moved the decimal point 1 space on the outside number, and you moved it one space on the inside number. As long as you remember to **move the decimal point an equal** number of spaces in **both** divisor and dividend, your answer will be correct. You can put in as many **ZERO PLACE HOLDERS** as you need.

☞ Use long division to solve these problems.

$$.4 \overline{)2}$$

$$.2 \overline{)732}$$

$$.7 \overline{).385}$$

$$.9 \overline{)747}$$

$$.5 \overline{)830}$$

$$8 \overline{)608}$$

$$.3 \overline{)5.688}$$

$$6 \overline{)29.88}$$

$$.7 \overline{)4788}$$

$$.8 \overline{)517.6}$$

$$9 \overline{)277.2}$$

$$.5 \overline{)2415}$$

DIVISION

PERFECTING THE POINT
★

☞ Use long division to solve these problems.

$.5\overline{)1352}$

$8\overline{)29.328}$

$.7\overline{)25.564}$

$9\overline{)216.45}$

$.4\overline{)30.324}$

$.2\overline{)1217.8}$

$.3\overline{)7758}$

$.6\overline{)167.4}$

$8\overline{)277.20}$

$.6\overline{)4944}$

$.4\overline{)203.32}$

$2\overline{)\$657.32}$

DIVISION

NAME_____

DATE_____

When you must check your division quotient (answer), you use the opposite skill - multiplication.

250.

check:

4.)100. becomes 4.)100.0.

250   quotient
x .4   divisor
_____
100.0.   dividend

Checking a problem containing decimals is no different than one with whole numbers. Remember to move the decimal point correctly in the checking problem.

☞ Check any 6 problems.

.3)201   .4)131.2   7)35.28   .8)1456

9)2214   .2)1006   .5)18.05   .6)434.4

PERFECTING THE POINT

DIVISION

NAME_____

DATE_____

You now have experience with numbers which divide evenly. But what happens if you have a remainder? **ZERO PLACE HOLDERS!**
You **add a zero place holder** to your remainder and **divide again**. If you still have a remainder, **add a zero and divide again**. If you still have a remainder, **add a zero and divide again**. Keep adding those zero place holders and dividing <u>until you get rid of that old remainder</u>. Sometimes, you will just have to add a zero place holder and divide one last time. Sometimes, you will need to repeat adding the zero and dividing several times. The good thing is you can add those zero place holders until the cows come home and always be ok. This is called **writing your remainder as a decimal.**

```
        .8725
   4)3.4900
    -32
     29
    -28
      10  first remainder + zero place holder
     - 8
      20  second remainder + zero place holder
     - 20
```

It may seem a bit of a bother, but you **never have a remainder**. Instead, you have a decimal.
You could even **round off** your quotient. Your answer could have been rounded off to the nearest tenth (.9), the nearest hundredth (.87) or the nearest thousandth (.873). When you are <u>told to round off</u>, just divide one place **past**, so you'll know whether to round up or not.

☞ Divide these numbers, rounding off to the **nearest tenth.**

89.33=89.3

3)268

.4)345

.5)802

6)637

.8)492

.7)504

9)763

.2)6.91

PERFECTING THE POINT

DIVISION

If you plan to round off, how do you check your problem? You check it _before_ you round off, with the **unrounded quotient**. If you wait until you have rounded off, your dividend won't match your checking problem's product. Then, you won't know if your quotient is right or wrong.

Always check the problem's <u>unrounded quotient</u>.

☞ Round all of your answers off to the **nearest hundredth**. Check any 8 problems.

$7\overline{)4.97}$

$.3\overline{)7.25}$

$9\overline{)333}$

$.4\overline{)296}$

$.5\overline{)7.38}$

$.8\overline{)2.10}$

$6\overline{)14}$

$.2\overline{)34.7}$

$.9\overline{)403}$

$5\overline{).637}$

$.3\overline{)4.26}$

$7\overline{)\$58.38}$

Occasionally, you do run into a problem that you could divide forever - and never finish it! This kind of a problem seems to never end (and probably doesn't). Remember the third (.33)? Back on page 28 of this workbook, we called the third a **repeating decimal**. What that means is that it has a **pattern** of numbers which **repeats over and over - and never ends**. The third is a repeating pattern of threes (.3333333 forever). Two thirds (.67) is really a repeating pattern of sixes that has been rounded off (.6666666=.67). Here is an example of a **repeating decimal**:

$$16.6666666$$

$$.6\,)\overline{10}\quad\text{becomes}\quad 6.\,)\overline{100.000000000}$$

When you are dividing, you will do yourself a big favor if you look for these **repeating patterns** in your **remainders**. Once you saw this six start repeating **in the remainders**, it was time to stop. You never will get anything different for an answer and never run out of the same remainder. If you get a remainder you've had before - STOP! You probably have a repeating decimal.

☞ Round off these decimals to the **nearest hundredth.**

$$.3\,)\overline{67}\qquad\qquad .6\,)\overline{45}\qquad\qquad 4\,)\overline{8.606}\qquad\qquad .9\,)\overline{500}$$

$$8\,)\overline{45}\qquad\qquad .5\,)\overline{.83}\qquad\qquad 6\,)\overline{28}\qquad\qquad 3\,)\overline{10}$$

☞ Since you are talking about people, round off to the nearest **whole**. Check any **4** answers.

1. The largest chocolate Easter egg weighed a bit over 7,561.75 lb. If each person were given a half pound (.5) piece, how many people would have chocolate? _____

2. The largest mince pie ever baked weighed 13,362.9 lb. If it was sliced into .3 lb. slices, how many people could be fed? _____

3. The largest custard pie weighed 448 lb. If it were divided into .3 lb. portions, how many people would it feed? _____

4. The world's largest popsicle weighed 5,750 lb. If customers were given a half pound each, how many people would it take to eat it up? _____

5. The longest salami weighed 863.5 lb. If each person were given a .6 lb. section, how many people could have a full piece? _____

6. In 1985, a 33,616.75 lb. ice cream sundae was created. If this were served into .7 lb. sundaes, how many people would get one? _____

7. Mrs. Miriam Hargrave failed 39 driving tests in 8 years. She averaged how many failures per year? _____ (She got the license on her 40th try!)

PERFECTING THE POINT

DIVISION

NAME _____

DATE _____

You do nothing different when dividing by a two place number. Move the decimal point enough places to make it a whole number and divide. Add **ZERO PLACE HOLDERS** when necessary.

$$
\begin{array}{r}
19.2 \\
.25\ \overline{)4.80}\ \text{becomes}\ 25.\overline{)480.0} \\
\underline{-25} \\
230 \\
\underline{-225} \\
50 \\
\underline{-50} \\
\end{array}
$$

Never leave a remainder. Divide until you are finished or one place past where you need to round off. Decimals **never** have remainders (like 4 R2).

☞ Round off all problems to the **nearest tenth**. Check any 5 problems.

$$1.9\ \overline{)485}$$

$$.53\ \overline{)20.9}$$

$$6.2\ \overline{)73}$$

$$14\ \overline{)359.8}$$

$$.73\ \overline{).295}$$

$$4.8\ \overline{)3.82}$$

$$.03\ \overline{).59}$$

$$2.5\ \overline{)900}$$

PERFECTING THE POINT

☞ Round off to the **nearest hundredth**. Check any **5** problems.

1. The largest hamburger on record weighed a bit over 5,005.75 lb. How many quarter pounders could be made from this whopper? _____

2. "The Chuck Wagon Gang's Chili Meat Pie" weighed 13,362.9 lb. If people were given a 1.2 lb. helping, how many people might get heartburn? _____

3. The record for a serving of mashed potatoes is 18,260 lb. If people got a .15 lb. serving, how many people could eat? _____

4. The longest continuous ballroom dancing record is 126 hrs. Twenty seven girls danced for an average of _____ hrs. per girl.

5. The fastest flamenco dancer ever measured performed 960 heel taps per minute. The 17 year-old tapped _____ times per second.

6. The highest recorded speed at which someone has received Morse code was 75.2 words per minute. How many words per second is this? _____

7. John Elkhay made 5,247 two-egg omelets in 36 hours. How many omelets did he make in an hour? _____ At the one hour rate, how many did he make in 5 hours? _____ In 12 hours? _____ In 25 hours? _____

PERFECTING THE POINT

DIVISION

To check multiplication problems, you divide. You can use **either** the multiplier or the multiplicand as the divisor. If you use the multiplier as the divisor, your quotient will be the multiplicand. If you use the multiplicand as your divisor, your multiplier will be the quotient. Therefore, use whichever number is easier to divide. Your product always should be the dividend.

$$\begin{array}{r} 2.35 \\ \times\ .2 \\ \hline .470 \end{array}$$ multiplicand / multiplier / product

$$2.2\overline{)\,.470}$$

$$.2\,\overline{)\,.470}$$

$$2.35\,\overline{)\,.470}$$

Again, check your answer **before** you round off. If you wait until after you have rounded, your check answer won't match your product.

☞ Solve these problems. Check each problem. Round to the nearest **hundredth**.

$$\begin{array}{r} 3.94 \\ \times\ .5 \\ \hline \end{array}$$

$$.4\,\overline{)\,528}$$

$$\begin{array}{r} .702 \\ \times\ .13 \\ \hline \end{array}$$

$$\begin{array}{r} 63.01 \\ \times\ .7 \\ \hline \end{array}$$

$$6.8\,\overline{)\,24.93}$$

$$\begin{array}{r} 9.672 \\ \times\ 3.1 \\ \hline \end{array}$$

$$\begin{array}{r} 25.097 \\ \times\ .6 \\ \hline \end{array}$$

$$\begin{array}{r} 8.324 \\ \times\ 2.5 \\ \hline \end{array}$$

You've already learned to multiply decimal numbers. When you multiplied a decimal number by a whole number, your product (answer) got larger. There is another **shortcut** for multiplying by the **whole numbers ending in zero** - ten, hundred, thousand, etc.

The old, long way of multiplication looks like the examples below. Notice that each product (answer) is larger than your beginning number (the multiplicand). Zeros at the end of the decimal numbers would be rounded off.

```
   1.34          1.34              1.34
 x   10        x  100            x 1000
  000           000               000
  134           000               000
 13.40          134               000
              134.00              134
                                1340.00
```

Or, you could use the **zero shortcut** taught in the Percents 1 section of this workbook. Again, zeros at the end of the decimal numbers round off.

```
   1.34          1.34              1.34
 x   10        x  100            x 1000
 13.40        134.00           1340.00
```

Or you could use this shortcut. Its steps include:
(1) Count the **number of places** that have a **zero at the end** of your multiplier (10 has one, 100 has two, and 1000 has three, etc.).
(2) Move the decimal point to the **right** that number of places (one place for 10, 2 places for 100, 3 places for 1000, etc.). Add zero place holders if necessary.

$$1.34 \times 10 = 1.3.40 \qquad 1.34 \times 100 = 1.34.00 \qquad 1.34 \times 1000 = 1.340.00$$

$$\quad\quad\quad\quad\quad\;\; 1 \qquad\qquad\qquad\qquad\quad 2 \qquad\qquad\qquad\qquad\qquad 3$$

---

(1) 2.46 x 100 =

(2) .39 x 1000 =

(3) .705 x 1000 =

(4) 49 x 10 =

(5) 6.3894 x 10 =

(6) .004 x 100 =

(7) 36.543 x 1000 =

(8) 5.608 x 100 =

(9) .05 x 10000 =

PERFECTING THE POINT

NAME _____

DATE _____

DIVISION

Remember the last sentence on the previous page? "Moving the decimal point the other way (**left**) would make your answer smaller."

In **division**, your **answer is smaller** when you divide by a whole number. Since division is the opposite of multiplication, you can use the same **shortcut** to divide by moving the decimal point in the **opposite** direction (**left**). Moving the decimal point to the left reduces your answer.

You follow essentially the same steps:

(1) Count the number of places containing a zero in your divisor (dividend ÷ divisor = quotient).

(2) Move your decimal point to the **left** the **same number of places** (10 moves ___ place, 100 moves ___ , 1000 moves ___ etc.).

$$1.34 \div 10 = .134 \qquad 1.34 \div 100 = .0134 \qquad 1.34 \div 1000 = .00134$$

Moving the decimal point will increase or decreases your answer, depending on the direction you move it. **Division decreases.** **Multiplication makes more.**

☞ Find these quotients by using the **decreasing shortcut.**

(1) 34.6 ÷ 100 =

(2) 29.4 ÷ 1000 =

(3) 7 ÷ 10 =

(4) 45.239 ÷ 100 =

(5) 32 ÷ 1000 =

(6) 50.04 ÷ 10 =

(7) .4 ÷ 100 =

(8) 9.34 ÷ 10000 =

☞ Pay attention to the signs. Move your decimal point correctly to solve these problems.

(9) 3.45 x 100 =

(10) 14.6 ÷ 1000 =

(11) 1.698 ÷ 100 =

(12) 5.0809 x 10 =

(13) 2.7603 x 1000 =

(14) 2.7603 ÷ 1000 =

As a review, you changed **percentages to decimals** by moving the decimal point _____ spaces to the _____.

$$15\% = .15$$

To change a <u>decimal number back</u> into a **percentage**, do the opposite by moving the decimal point in the **opposite direction**. To change **decimals to percentages**, move the decimal point **<u>2 spaces to the right</u>** and add the percent (%) sign. Don't forget the percent sign (%) or your answer will be wrong. For example:

$$.15 = 15\%$$

☞ Write these decimals as percentages.

1) .23 =_____   2) .44 =_____

3) .08 =_____   4) .50 =_____

5) .09 =_____   6) .03 =_____

7) .71 =_____   8) .05 =_____

9) .04 =_____   10) .99 =_____

☞ If your decimal number has more than 2 digits in it, that's ok. Move your decimal point the same **2 spaces to the right**.

11) .094 =_____   12) .632 =_____

13) .5025 =_____   14) .0075 =_____

15) .0633 =_____   16) .1435 =_____

17) .905 =_____   18) .0567 =_____

19) .0005 =_____   20) .3870 =_____

21) .45 =_____   22) .0055 =_____

23) .7803 =_____   24) .85 =_____

25) .3006 =_____   26) .001 =_____

Reproduction restricted.

☞ If you have a decimal with a single digit, make it into a 2 digit number by adding a **ZERO PLACE HOLDER**. Then you'll have 2 digits and can move the decimal point **2 spaces to the right**.

1) .5 =_____   2) .9 =_____

3) .2 =_____   4) .7 =_____

5) .6 =_____   6) .3 =_____

7) .893 =_____   8) .02 =_____

9) .4 =_____   10) .0966 =_____

☞ Write these decimals as a percent. Then write the meaning in words.
    example: .5 = **50%** = **fifty percent**   .365 = **36.5%** = **thirty-six and one half percent**

11) .9 =_____ = _____

12) .47 =_____ = _____

13) .0825 =_____ = _____

14) .9333 =_____ = _____

15) .3 =_____ = _____

16) .655 =_____ = _____

17) .007 =_____ = _____

18) .025 =_____ = _____

19) .1 =_____ = _____

20) .9275 =_____ = _____

21) .0025 =_____ = _____

☞ Sometimes, you are given a number which has both whole and decimal places. These numbers can also be written as a percent. Follow the rule of moving the decimal point **2 spaces to the right**. Numbers like these are occasionally used when talking about inflation (prices going up) or the economy. When something doubles, it goes up 200% (2 wholes), triples (300% = 3 wholes), etc.

example: 1.45 = **145%**   2.005 = **200.5% (two hundred and one half of one percent)**

1) 3.04 =_____   2) 4.5 =_____

3) 1.255 =_____   4) 6.009 =_____

5) .329 =_____   6) .2 =_____

7) .004 =_____   8) 3.1 =_____

9) .0175 =_____   10) .68 =_____

☞ Now review everything you've learned about switching percents to decimals and decimals to percents. If the number is a percent, switch it to a decimal. If the number is written as a decimal, switch it to a percent.

example: 19.8% = **.198**   .198 = **19.8%**

11) 14.35% =_____   12) .98 =_____

13) .245 =_____   14) 2% =_____

15) .003 =_____   16) 2.09 =_____

17) 4.75% =_____   18) 99.99% =_____

19) 3.0667 =_____   20) 250.6% =_____

21) .004% =_____   22) .004 =_____

23) .0025 =_____   24) .25% =_____

25) 1% =_____   26) 1 =_____

27) 50% =_____   28) .005 =_____

In PERCENTS 1, you learned how to find the percentage of a number (ex: 5% of 250). Now you are ready to find the percentage of a number when it isn't given to you. For example:

Jane had an ice cream party. She bought 5 cartons of ice cream. Her guests finished 3 of the cartons. What percentage did they eat?_____

When you knew the percentage, you multiplied. When the problem doesn't tell you the percentage and asks you to find it, you **do the opposite - <u>divide</u>**.

In this problem, you have two numbers - the <u>5</u> possible cartons and the <u>3</u> that they finished. How do you know which number to divide into the other?   Use a little logical thinking. If you divide the 3 into the 5 ($3\overline{)5}$), you will get an answer bigger than a whole. An answer bigger than one whole would mean they ate all of the ice cream (100%) plus the decimal remainder (67%). Her guests couldn't eat 167% of the ice cream when **only 100% was available**. Therefore, you don't divide the smaller number into the bigger number.

Because they didn't eat all (100%) of the ice cream, you must <u>**divide the bigger number into the smaller number**</u>. Put in your understood decimal point and add as many zero place holders as you need to finish the problem.

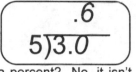

Your answer is .6, but is that written as a percent? No, it isn't. Change your quotient into a percent by moving your decimal point _____ spaces to the _____. Write your percent sign after the number (60%) and you have your answer. The guests ate 60% of the ice cream.

These are the two important facts to remember when finding an unknown percent:

1) ALWAYS divide the larger number into the smaller number -
because most percentages are less than one whole (100%).
2) Change your division answer (quotient) back into a percent by
moving the decimal point *2 spaces to the right*.

☞   Divide the problems. Then change your quotients into percentages.

$$6\overline{).9} \qquad 4\overline{).2} \qquad .3\overline{).3} \qquad .5\overline{).4}$$

$$5\overline{).7} \qquad 2\overline{).8} \qquad 8\overline{)4} \qquad 9\overline{)1.8}$$

DATE_____

☞ Write your quotients as a percent. Check any 15 problems.

$.4 \overline{).26}$ $7 \overline{)2.8}$ $5 \overline{)3.4}$ $6 \overline{)5.4}$

$.8 \overline{).43}$ $9 \overline{)8.19}$ $2 \overline{).83}$ $3 \overline{).51}$

$26 \overline{)3.9}$ $4.5 \overline{).765}$ $.32 \overline{).96}$ $5 \overline{)3.7}$

$63 \overline{)8.82}$ $7.1 \overline{)1.846}$ $2.4 \overline{).840}$ $8 \overline{).436}$

$5 \overline{).932}$ $.6 \overline{).1854}$ $4.3 \overline{).2881}$ $52 \overline{)26.26}$

There is another way to say the same problem when the **percent is missing**.

6 is what % of 30

You follow the same two steps.

    (1) Divide the larger number into the smaller number.

    (2) Move your decimal point in your quotient **2 spaces to the right**.

Now you have the answer to your **missing percentage**.

$$.2 = 20\%$$
$$30\overline{)6.0}$$

☞ Find the missing percentage. Round off to the nearest <u>hundredth</u> of a percent, when necessary.

1) 8 is what % of 24

2) 10 is what % of 40

3) 7 is what % of 28

4) 5 is what % of 45

5) 6 is what % of 24

6) 18 is what % of 45

7) 2 is what % of 4

8) 4 is what % of 32

9) 14 is what % of 28

10) 15 is what % of 60

11) 24 is what % of 36

12) 25 is what % of 75

Word problems give you the information you need. But sometimes, the word problem wants you to solve for information it didn't give you. Here's an example:

Marcy has 16 dolls in her collection. Eleven have blonde hair. What percentage of her dolls are not blonde?_____

Remember the **complementary numbers**? You know that 11 out of the 16 are not the answer you need because they are blondes. So, 16-11= 5 (the answer you must find). Add enough zero place holders to finish dividing.

$$16\overline{)5.0000} = .3125$$

.3125 =31.25%

Suppose that the problem had another question added onto the end of it?

Blondes represent what percentage?_____

You can solve this two ways. You are talking about all 16 dolls, 11 blondes and 5 non-blondes. You could divide the 16 into the 11 that you know are blondes. Or you could subtract the non-blonde percentage (31.25%) from **100%** (all of the dolls). Either way will give you the correct answer.

$$16\overline{)11.0000} = .6875 = 68.75\%$$

100.00%
-31.25 non-blonde
68.75% blonde

☞ Find the missing percentage(s). Round to the nearest **whole percent**.

1) Max has 18 stamps from Germany. Ten are postmarked Hamburg. What percentage is from other cities?_____

2) Leslie has 26 spoons in her collection. Eighteen are from the US. What percentage is from other countries?_____
What percentage is from the US?_____

3) Fred raises show dogs. He has 18 dogs, 12 of which are females. What percentage of his dogs is male?_____
Female?_____

4) Susan is memorizing Philippians 2. She has memorized 12 of the 30 verses. What percentage has she learned?__
What percentage does she have left to memorize?_____

☞ CHALLENGE PAGE. Find the missing percentages. Round to the nearest **tenth of a percent**.

1) Stephen collects model cars. He built 14 of his 32 models. What percentage of his models were built by someone else?_____ By Stephen?_____

2) Laura has 25 stuffed animals. Her favorites are the 8 bears and 5 horses. What percentage of her animals are bears?_____ Horses?_____ Favorites?_____

3) James went to a 30 item salad bar. He made a salad, using 18 items. What percentage did he use in his salad?_____ How many did he skip?_____

4) Marsha had a craft display of 35 items. She sold 9 in the morning and 7 in the afternoon. What percentage was sold in the morning?_____ Afternoon?_____ All day?_____ What percentage was left?_____

5) Leon helps in the family store. He had 45 cases to shelve. Saturday morning, he finished shelving 20 cases. What percentage <u>still needs shelving</u>?_____

6) Mitzi has 34 elephants in her collection. Twelve are carved from wood, 2 are porcelain, 8 are plastic, 3 are wax, 5 are pewter, and 4 are marble. What percentage is wax?_____ Plastic?_____ Marble?_____
Porcelain?____ Pewter?_____ Wood?_____

7) The bird sanctuary has 48 birds. Eight are nocturnal (night animals) and the remainder are diurnal (day animals). What percentage is nocturnal?_____ Diurnal?_____

Now that you have learned about decimals, there is a **shortcut** you can use when **dividing large numbers**. You can use this **shortcut** with two kinds of problems - those looking for percentages and those that have nothing to do with a percentage. Here is a sample word problem that would be no fun to work without the shortcut:

Paul has 500 stamps in his collection. He has 270 from the U.S., 100 from Europe, and 130 from Asia and Africa. What percentage of his collection is from the U.S.?_____ Europe?_____

No one likes to divide by three place numbers, especially when one or more of the places contain a zero. One way you can **shorten long divisors** is to use a **zero shortcut**. Move your divisor's decimal point so the zeros are no longer necessary. Then move the dividend's decimal point in the **same direction**, for the **same number of places**.

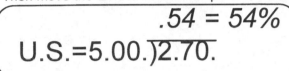

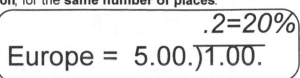

In this example, move **both** the divisor's and dividend's decimal points **2 spaces to the left** _before_ you divide. The zeros are no longer necessary and your divisor becomes 5 instead of 500. Your dividend is also reduced by an equal proportion. By moving the decimal point 2 places, you have essentially reduced both sides 100 times before you ever started dividing. Now divide and get your quotient.

If you weren't looking for a percentage, you'd be done. But in this problem, you are looking for a percentage. Move the decimal point 2 places **back to the right** to change your decimal quotient into a percentage.

Remember, you only use this method to get rid of **unwanted zeros in long divisors**.

☞ Use the shortcut method above to solve these problems. Round to the nearest **tenth of a percent**.

1) Ed has 200 pennies in his collection. He has 8 steel pennies, 158 wheat pennies, and the remainder in Lincolns. What percentage of his pennies are wheat?_____ Steel?_____ Lincolns?_____

2) Ford has 50 scriptures to memorize this year. He has memorized 28. What percentage has he completed?_____ What percentage does he still need to learn?_____

3) Sonya's piano book contains 200 pages. She completed page 128 today. What percentage has she completed?____ What percentage is left to complete?_____

4) Gideon's army originally had 32,000 men. God reduced it to 300 soldiers. What percentage fought?_____

☞ CHALLENGE PAGE. Find these quotients. Round to the nearest **tenth**.

1) The Lord commanded Moses to count all of the male Levites, one month and older (NUMBERS 3). There were 22,000 in all. Of these, 6,200 were Merarites, 8,600 were Kohathites, and 7,500 were Gershonites. Which was the largest clan?_____ What percentage were the Gershonites?_____ Merarites?_____ Kohathites?_____

2) God ordered Moses to take a census, counting all males 20 years and older who could serve in the army (NUMBERS 1). In the first census, Joseph's descendants consisted of 2 tribes. Manasseh had 32,200 men and Ephraim had 40,500. How many descendants did Joseph have?_____ What percent were from Ephraim?_____ Manasseh?_____

3) At the time of second census, Manasseh had 52,700 fighting men and Ephraim 32,500 (NUMBERS 26:28-37). How many male descendants were there?_____ The tribe of Manasseh (increased/decreased)_____ since the first census? The tribe of Ephraim (increased/decreased) since the first census. In the 2nd census, what percentage were from the tribe of Manasseh?_____ Ephraim?_____

4) The Lord ordered the plunder from the Midianites (NUMBERS 31:25-54) to be divided between the soldiers and the community. One out of every 500 was set apart for the Lord. They had 337,500 sheep, 36,000 cattle, 30,500 donkeys, and 16,000 people. How many sheep were given to the Lord?_____ Cattle?_____ Donkeys?_____ People?_____

Reproduction restricted.

Americans are becoming more aware of what they eat. Nutritious, healthy foods make you feel better and the body God gave you last longer. High calorie foods, which cause fat to be produced in your body, are not good for "God's Temple".

Health professionals recommend that fat supply no more than 30% of your daily calories. On the average, Americans get a whopping 46% of their daily calories from fat. This excess fat can cause heart disease and other complications.

Each gram of fat takes 9 calories of body heat to burn it up. If you eat more grams of fat than your body burns, the extra will be stored in your body as fat. Protein and carbohydrates take less than half as long to burn up because each calorie equals only 4 grams. Fat, with its 9 calories per gram, is very fattening.

Let's look at some dairy foods. These facts are taken from the label. We will find out what percentage of the calories are fat calories in whole milk.

Whole milk contains 150 calories and 8 grams of fat in one cup

We know that each gram of fat = 9 calories so   8 g. x 9 calories = 72 calories

72 equals what % of 150

$$\frac{.48 = 48\%}{150\overline{)72.00}}$$

The steps are as follows:

(1) Read your label. Find the calories and the fat grams.

(2) Calculate how many calories your fat grams equal.

(3) Find the percentage.

Is whole milk good for you? That depends. It has vitamins and 30% of your daily calcium needs. But so do all of the other lower fat milk products. Let's look at some other milk products and compare.

☞ Find the percentage of fat in the following dairy products. Round to the nearest **tenth of a percent**. All facts are for 8 oz./1 cup servings. (g. = gram)

1) 2% milk has 120 calories and 5 g. fat =_____

2) $\frac{1}{2}$% milk has 90 calories and 1 g. of fat =_____

3) your brand of milk has _____calories and _____ g. fat =____

4) plain lowfat yogurt has 140 calories and 4 g. fat =_____

☞ These items are per 1 oz. serving.

5) sour cream has 52 calories and 5 g. fat =_____

6) mayonnaise has 200 calories and 22 g. fat =_____

7) cheddar cheese has 115 calories and 9 g. fat =_____

8) _____ and _____ had the highest fat percentages.

☞ Find the fat percentages (g. = grams) in these items. Round to the nearest **tenth of a percent**.

1) flavored cream cheese = 90 calories and 8 g. of fat =____

2) plain cream cheese = 100 calories and 10 g. of fat =____

3) 100% corn oil margarine = 70 calories and 7 g. fat =____

4) your margarine has ____ calories and ____ g. of fat =____

5) bacon (2 slices) = 90 calories and 8 g. of fat =_____

6) chicken (3 oz.) = 115 calories and 4 g. of fat =_____

7) egg noodles (1 cup) = 200 calories and 1 g. of fat =_____

8) peanut butter (2 Tbl.) = 180 calories and 16 g. of fat=____

9) butter (1 Tbl.) = 100 calories and 12 g. of fat =_____

10) french dressing (1 Tbl.) = 65 calories and 6 g. fat =____

11) your favorite salad dressing =____ calories ___g. fat =____

12) egg (1 large) has 80 calories and 6 grams of fat =_____

☞ Use your answers above to answer the following questions.

13) The two <u>lowest</u> fat percentages were in _____ and _____

14) Between chicken and bacon, which is better for you?_____

15) Go to the store and find five other items to fill in this chart.

Item	Brand	serving size	calories	fat (grams)	percentage of fat

Americans consume an average of 128 pounds of sugar each year. This is about 635 calories per day. Some of the sugar you add to foods. Other sugars are hidden in the everyday foods you eat.

Fruits are high in natural sugars and are good for you (if you aren't diabetic). Other foods are high in sugars which are not good for you. Sugar causes cavities and overweight, a bad combination.

On labels, manufacturers must list the ingredients in order, from most to least. The ingredient which is used the most occurs first in the list. The ingredient used the least is listed last. Manufacturers disguise sugar by giving it many names. Honey, corn syrup, molasses, maple syrup, and brown sugar are a few. The "ose" brothers - sucrose, fructose, glucose, dextrose, lactose, and maltose - make up the majority of the other names. Sugar is sugar, no matter what it is called. When sugar is mentioned toward the first of the list, there is more sugar in the serving.

Cereals are sneaky. They have the ingredients listed, but also need another listing toward the bottom. They must list "sucrose and other sugars" by weight. To most people, those grams mean nothing. But to the educated nutritionist, every **3 grams equals 1 teaspoon of sugar**! And if you add sugar to that cereal - wow!

Let's look at a cereal advertised as "lower in sugar than most children's cereals".

SERVING SIZE: 1 OZ. (about 1/3 cup) - which is very little cereal when measured
SUCROSE AND OTHER SUGARS: 7 GRAMS (NO MILK)   13 GRAMS (1/2 C. skim)

Unless you like your cereal dry, you must figure the grams with the milk. It takes 3 grams for every teaspoon, so divide the 13 grams by 3.

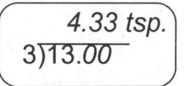

$$\begin{array}{r} 4.33 \text{ tsp.} \\ 3\overline{)13.00} \end{array}$$

So that tiny single serving of cereal with 1/2 cup of skim milk contains 4 and one third teaspoons of sugar. Measure that amount of sugar into a bowl by itself and you will be surprised.

☞ Find the cereals' sugar content (with milk). Then go to the store and find five of your own.

Cereal Name	Serving size	Calories with milk	Sucrose and other sugars		Sugar tsp.
			no milk	1/2 cup skim milk	
H	1 cup	150	9g.	15g.	____
S	1/2 cup	130	6g.	12g.	____
O	1/3 cup	150	8g.	14g.	____
G	7/8 cup	150	5g.	11g.	____
A (Nutri-sweet)	1/2 cup	90	0g.	6g.	____
_____	_____	_____	_____	_____	____
_____	_____	_____	_____	_____	____
_____	_____	_____	_____	_____	____
_____	_____	_____	_____	_____	____

There is another way to use your division skills in working with percentages.

6 is 50% of what number?

Follow these steps.
  (1) Divide the **percentage** into the other number. Sometimes the percentage is larger and sometimes it isn't.
  (2) Move the decimal point in your quotient **2 spaces to the right**. You also may use the zero shortcut, if you wish.

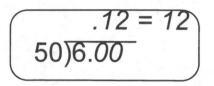

$$.12 = 12$$
$$50\overline{)6.00}$$

Notice that this time, your answer **is not** a percent. The percent was already in your problem. You used it as the divisor. **Your quotient can't be another percent.**

☞ Find the missing number.

1) 8 is 25% of what number?   2) 4 is 50% of what number?

3) 16 is 10% of what number?   4) 45 is 90% of what number?

5) 25 is 5% of what number?   6) 30 is 75% of what number?

7) 9 is 10% of what number?   8) 20 is 20% of what number?

9) 35 is 25% of what number?   10) 50 is 1% of what number?

11) 60 is 75% of what number?   12) 30 is 60% of what number?

13) 40 is 80% of what number?   14) 1 is 10% of what number?

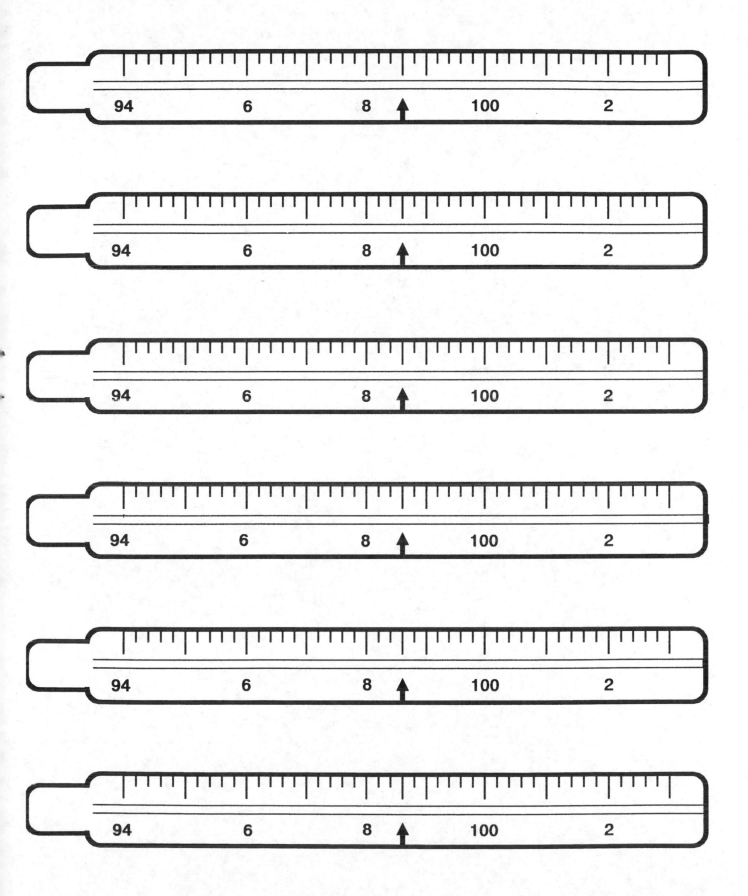

Certificate of Achievement

_____

knows
percentages
and decimals!

Mastery Publications

_____
WITNESS

_____
DATE

Perfecting the Point